THE LAST
SEX MANUAL

THE LAST
SEX MANUAL

✕✕✕✕✕

Ron Pion, M.D.
with Jerry Hopkins

Wyden Books

Names and identifying details have been changed throughout this book to assure the privacy of those concerned.

MANUFACTURED IN THE UNITED STATES OF AMERICA

First Edition

Trade distribution by Simon and Schuster
A Division of Gulf + Western Corporation
New York, New York 10020

Library of Congress Cataloging in Publication Data

Pion, Ronald J.
    The last sex manual.

    1. Sex. 2. Sex instruction. I. Hopkins,
Jerry, joint author. II. Title.
HQ31.P638   301.41'8   77-25539
ISBN 0-671-22958-3

Contents

Introduction:
Is This Really It?

"The last sex manual," huh? Who says? Well, I say that it *could* be. You see, over the past 12 years my colleagues and I have experienced extraordinary success in treating the ten most common sexual complaints, using a method of counseling that is private, quick, and practically without cost. And for the past three years we have been sharing our behavior-changing process with members of the medical profession in seminars over much of the U.S. and Canada. Only recently have we developed a means by which the reader may use the same quick process, alone or with a partner, in the privacy of his (or her or their) own home.

I believe it is important to emphasize the speed with which my clients move from sexual dissatisfaction to sexual satisfaction as a rule. I do not see people more than four times; and many whom I see stop coming after only two or three visits, because their problems simply have ceased to exist or have ceased to be recognized as problems (while other troubled persons with similar or virtuallly identical complaints who see more traditional therapists are still in the initial stages of assessment). Some of my clients I've never even met—the successful counseling has been conducted entirely by mail.

I don't claim the techniques in this book will work for everyone. No one, not even Masters and Johnson and some of the other qualified sex therapists, can promise 100 percent success. But I do know that this process will work for many, especially those who have failed when they tried other techniques. I believe that chances are excellent, in fact, that *just reading this book* will put a troubled reader securely on the road to better health and greater sexual satisfaction.

Part of what I offer is not going to make me many friends in the therapeutic establishment. (Many do not like self-help books at all.) You see, I am offering a learning process that makes breaking old habits unnecessary and adding new ones fun. And I say it isn't even important to understand the problem. Not only is this in sharp contrast to the traditional psychoanalytic view (which holds that underlying psychological conflicts are responsible for the symptoms and have to be straightened out before the sex problem can be eliminated); it also goes against most other theories of sex therapy (which use behavior techniques to "unlearn" the symptom).

Along with "unlearning" and deep, long-lasting psychological or psychoanalytic probing I also throw out all talk of "motivation." Instead I call upon readiness, purpose*full*ness, and hope*full*ness (notice the way the last two are spelled), personality traits that are easily recognized, nurtured, and used well.

I provide an imaginary scale on which the troubled reader may weigh, or evaluate, his or her sexuality. This assists my clients to know where they are—that's the problem—and to determine where they want to go—that's the goal.

I offer what I think is an engrossing, entertaining game to play, called Up Your Orgasm. This enables the troubled reader to step into his own future by creating productive fantasy.

The best things I have in my bag of tricks aren't mine at all. These are the stories I have collected over the years from sexual "winners" who used to be sexual "losers." I let them show exactly how they changed. So the reader who wants to experience orgasm, for example, can get it straight from others who once were in the same position and who are there no longer. These are the best teachers that the sexual experience can produce.

I think the critics and many members of the medical profession may miss the point of this book, and I think the people are going to get it.

THE LAST
SEX MANUAL

CHAPTER

1

How I Got from There to Here (Part I)

I grew up believing in sexual bogeymen (bogey persons?). I don't have any of those creatures in me now, but I remember only too vividly when it was not that way. I was as confused a teen-ager and young adult as the very "best" I've ever met since. I came out of the same mystique. I want you to know that I was raised no differently. Sexual dysphoria (doctor talk for, "It isn't working the way I want it to") was being set up in my life just as it was in everybody else's.

I remember finding a box of condoms on the school playground and embarrassing myself in class by trying to blow them up. (Though I was in junior high school, I honestly didn't know what they were.) I remember getting caught sneaking peeks into the dressing room of my parents' lingerie store. I remember being in absolute awe of one of the basketball players when I heard he was having sex regularly with a nice girl. I remember filing away huge quantities of false information, while learning to tell jokes and brag outlandishly about fictitious conquests. And so I passed into manhood.

What bothers me today is that it didn't have to be that way—for me or for anyone else. Kids didn't have to be told all those incredible lies about masturbation. Kids didn't have to begin puberty and grow breasts and hair and start to bleed without any preparation. Kids didn't have to be given dozens of reasons *not* to do something that felt so good—remember them?

"Billy, you'll get in trouble, you'll get a horrible disease if you do that."

"Sally, you'll get pregnant if you do that."

"David, you'll throw away your life if you get somebody pregnant and have to get married. You won't be able to go to college."

"Debbie, only whores do that! Nice girls never . . ."

On and on the warnings went. And no one ever said anything nice. Adults as a general rule haven't been nice to kids. I mean, if sex is something that could be beautiful —and there are a number of poets, anyway, who think that's so—then why start it in such a smutty way? Why not say it's beautiful?

Things began to change for me, radically, when I was in medical school at the University of California at Los Angeles (UCLA), while studying for a practice in general medicine, then serving a residency in obstetrics and gynecology. I remember when I was still a med student and we were learning how to give a woman a pelvic examination. There were six of us standing in line—all six of us were, one at a time, going to stick our fingers in. I'd never come upon a vagina this way before.

Later I read a book called *The Men in White*, by André Suberain. There's a scene in the book where there's a group of students with the professor in a class in diagnosis or physical medicine. An attractive woman is asked to disrobe. A medical student recalls how suddenly he stopped being a medical student studying diagnosis and turned into being a voyeur. And then he caught himself in the moment and he was so caught up with guilt . . . and so I found in the novel someone else who felt the same way I did. The point is, I found this in a novel. Nobody at the medical school was saying anything about such things to us. Sexuality was never, ever mentioned, by anyone for any reason. No one was addressing himself or herself to the future doctor as a sexual human being. My teachers were letting me down.

Nor did I get much assistance from available texts. As a first-year resident I went to dormitories and fraternity and sorority houses to talk about pregnancy and delivery and I took pictures with me of births. This was in 1958, before the days of the pill and the IUD. I was single and I had a lot of time (I still do) and I was willing to talk in the evenings, so I made the speakers' list. This wasn't like being John Dean or Ralph Nader; it was more a way to get a free meal or meet a girl. I presented myself to these people as an expert on reproduction. You know what? I *was* an expert on reproduction, but the majority of the questions I got were about sex, and that was something I knew practically nothing about. I noticed that that didn't make much sense. At first I said I'd have the answer on my next visit, thinking I could find whatever I needed to know in a book. But that wasn't so. In 1958 there weren't the same kind of manuals which are so readily available today.

My mentors weren't much help, either. As a resident I worked in a clinic for pregnant women. Day after day I saw dozens and dozens of women, routinely checking them for kidney infections, swollen ankles, high blood pressure, and other frequently found symptoms of disease. Into this setting one day comes a woman in her eighth-and-a-half month. She looks up at me as I'm finishing the examination form, and she's normal and I heard the fetal heart. I checked her ankles, and everything's okay, and she says, "How about cunnilingus?"

Without even looking at her or thinking or anything, I said, "Sure."

Now, I was 26 at the time and I'm not certain I'd ever heard the word spoken before, although I vaguely knew what it meant. So after she left, I went and I knocked on the door of the senior resident and I said, "About this woman who was here, I have a hunch I know what she was talking about, but I'm not sure. She said, 'Is cunnilingus okay?' and I said, 'Sure.' Did I do right?"

The senior resident said, "Yuccch!"

Not all of my teachers and mentors were duds. There was a department of psychosomatic medicine at UCLA run by a guy named Charlie Wahl, and I was in awe of the way Charlie could speak with patients. He came on rounds and he asked questions that we never asked. He'd walk up to a woman in traction and say, "If I could give you three wishes right now, what would you wish for?"

I used to think, "What kind of talk is *that* for a doctor?" I mean, we were taught to ask if they had allergies and if they had had any operations and if it hurt and where— everything in the present or past. Then Charlie Wahl came along and took these people into the future. And it seemed to make them feel better, so I came to wonder: if people *feel* better, aren't they? When you're sick, isn't the future one of the best things you've got going? Surely the present's no fun.

I had the opportunity to audit psychiatry, and a lot of what happened to me that I considered good was directly attributable to Joshua Golden, a good friend and capable psychiatrist on the UCLA staff, who let me grow. He and I became bachelor friends, working colleague friends. He was a resident when I started in as an intern and later, after he did two years in the air force, he returned to the university faculty and I was an obstetrics resident. We did rounds together. And we had a weekly session where we'd bring in problem people and not-so-problemed people and put them together. Inevitably, the not-so-problemed people were soon solving the problems of the problem people.

This is how it happened. As a resident—as I've mentioned already—I was responsible for an assigned case load of prenatal patients, so for several months my mornings and afternoons were filled with pregnant women. There were other residents with similar case loads and we noticed that many of us became quickly disenchanted with our outpatient responsibilities. Too many patients, insufficient time allotted to develop that intangible quality known as "rapport," and the general boredom attendant on routine service added up to much disappointment. Add to this a resident's desire to seek out and stamp out pathology rather than his burning enthusiasm for "health maintenance and promotion," and you have an idea of what training programs were like throughout the United States. (This was in 1959; it hasn't changed much since.)

With the permission of my department chairman, Josh Golden and I proposed a program of group care. I would still be responsible for a specified clinic case load, but instead of seeing patients individually for maybe five minutes apiece, we would see them collectively, eight to ten at a time, for 40 to 45 minutes, over coffee. A sympathetic nurse was recruited—to record blood pressures and weights and to screen urine specimens prior to the sessions and add a professional woman's view during them —and we were off and talking.

All the women had pregnancy in common, so it didn't

matter who we scheduled, although we tried for a cross section, so there'd be "experienced" women there along with the first-timers. "Modeling" was going on. Vicarious learning. When a woman asked the kind of question that I could in no way answer from experience, I referred the question to one of the experienced mothers in the room. A 19-year-old, fearful of having her first baby, would ask about such and such and I'd say, "Wait a minute . . . Mary, you tell her." And if I didn't like what Mary was saying, I'd say, "Gretchen, do you believe that?" and Gretchen might say, "Hell, no, Mary, you're wrong; stop scaring the poor girl."

I usually didn't plan the content of the sessions. Reading materials were suggested for between sessions. And a permissive, information-sharing atmosphere was fostered. The participants proved most helpful to one another. Anxiety-laden topics were frequently introduced by the women and/or by our telling stories that we obtained previously from others. Sexual relationships before pregnancy and problems relating to pregnancy's influence on those relationships were discussed in an attempt to anticipate potential conflicts and, by so doing, avoid them.

I kept winning. I kept introducing all those successful people to all those people who thought they were losing by being pregnant. Let's face it, there are a lot of people who are fearful of being pregnant. The questions that first-time-pregnant women ask are as valid as they are predictable: "If I'm not supposed to be fearful, why am I seeing the doctor? If to be pregnant is to be normal, what's prenatal care about? And then there's the March of Dimes, with its defects-every-minute-in-America campaign. I mean, you've *got* to be scared if you're pregnant—else, why is this whole hospital system so interested in you?"

These were questions the first-timers shared in common. The two- and three- and four-time pregnant women handled all such anxiety easily, teaching much to the others. They were putting the uneasy at ease. I was watching "winners" and "losers" help everyone win.

At the same time, I had learned to stay with the prospective mother throughout the labor, or at least for as long as she was in labor in the hospital. Nearly always the husband was there, too. Now, I had few responsibilities away from the hospital, I liked people, and I didn't play golf, so I hung out with these couples.

I wanted to entertain people, especially between contractions, so I talked about my other interests—sex education in the schools, contraceptive education, and all that had to do with communication between people, and behavior modification. Talking was easy for me, and I guess I can say I was successful because I entertained. That is, I diverted or purposefully directed their attention away from the discomfort or whatever. It was a hypnotic technique, without the hypnosis. The more interesting the stories that I told, of course, the less noticeable was whatever, except during the height of contraction . . . and the more comfortable the women (and husbands) became.

I discovered that these men and women talked most frankly. They responded to my most candid probing with an openness that was (at first) as surprising as it was refreshing. When you spend several hours with two people who are in the highly charged emotional state that accompanies imminent childbirth, the intimacy seems natural. It flows. I asked them about sex and they talked and talked.

I remember the first time something like that happened, I was responsible for watching over a ward at night and was drawn to a visiting grandmother who was 76. I asked question after question of this woman. We became friendly, and in time it felt comfortable for me to ask her if she still did "it."

Smiling, she said, "I sure do, sonny."

I said, "And you obviously enjoy making love."

She said, "I sure do, sonny." Still smiling.

I leaned closer and asked, "Do you remember a time when you *didn't* enjoy it?"

The woman sat up. "Sonny," she exclaimed, "could I tell you stories . . ."

I said, "*Please* . . . tell me."

That's how I began my collection of "winners'" stories.

I won a fellowship in reproductive endocrinology and went to Sweden for a year, where I worked in one of the "hottest" steroid labs in the world, one that was getting attention from the Ford and Rockefeller Foundations and the National Institutes of Health and the World Health Organization. The hope of population pundits was focused on labs like this. For a year I did experimental work there and continued to learn from those people called patients.

The next year I returned to the U.S. with my wife Gail (whom I had met and married while at UCLA), where, beginning in 1964 as a faculty person at the University of Washington Medical School in Seattle, I did obstetrics and gynecological surgery and taught medical students and residents. More important, Gail set up an abortion counseling service on the telephone, and I assisted in getting Rockefeller money to establish a division of family planning and human sexuality in the university's department of obstetrics and gynecology, the first such curriculum in the country. And I met Ned Wagner.

Ned is a big bear of a man, a psychologist and friend, and what I want to let you know about Ned are some Ned Wagner stories. For example, Ned once was asked to see a person who wanted an abortion. She was a quadraplegic, who got pregnant a year or so after an accident that left her paralyzed from the neck down. She already had a couple of kids. Our department did abortions only for psychiatric reasons in those days, and she did not wish as a quadraplegic to take on the responsibility of a pregnancy and a new child. Of course Ned approved her abortion, but he wanted to know more about her relationship.

He said, "Obviously you've had sexual intercourse since the accident. Would you mind sharing with me so that I might share your success with other people?"

She said she had been anxious to resume sex because of her concern for her husband's need. No one had talked about sex to her while she was recuperating and in therapy. No one seemed concerned about her sexuality or any of the needs she and her husband might have. Finally, months later, she said something to her husband about it and he said, "Don't think about that."

She insisted, and so they talked and in time they resumed lovemaking. She said she was feeling good about it, too, because she noticed that her husband was experiencing what appeared to be joy. She also noticed that she didn't actually feel much—except emotionally. The paralysis saw to that.

She'd never practiced oral-genital sex before the accident, but afterward she wanted to try it. She noticed that kissing her husband's lips was full of feeling and so, in addition to kissing his lips, she now wanted to kiss his genitals. She started to do that, while still offering herself to traditional intercourse.

She said she had something she wanted to ask Ned. "Tell me," she said, "I can feel and enjoy kissing his genitals even *more* than vaginal sex—is that all right?"

When Ned told me that story, tears were streaming down his face.

Now Ned Wagner was keeping a notebook of successful stories. We began trading these stories the way little boys used to trade bubble-gum cards.

All the stories and experiences fit together, like countries on a map. I noticed that most people believed that medicine was *supposed* to taste awful, and that if it didn't taste that way it probably wasn't very good. I noticed that the austerity and uniformity and lack of imagination in hospital decor possibly was in itself hindering some patients' recovery. When I was growing up in Brooklyn, the family doctor made house calls, became a family friend, and now I noticed that two of the most revered of medical traditions—house calls and a bedside manner— were vanishing as quickly as the Age of the Specialist and the Computer came in. I noticed that it might make sense to get back to the basics—away from disease-oriented medicine and toward people-oriented medicine. Thus Ned Wagner and I—and others I met later—began to look to the healthy for guidance.

Of course we weren't alone. We had, in fact, been preceded by many others some years before.

CHAPTER
2
How I Got from There to Here (Part II)

Preceding us were the developers of what came to be called "humanistic psychology"—an approach to the study of human nature that stresses the uniqueness of the individual, focuses on the value, rights, dignity, responsibilities, and fulfillment of the person, and assumes that true health is the result of realizing one's full potential.

When I found these people, these forward-thinking pioneers, I felt the gratitude of Robinson Crusoe when he saw Friday's footprints in the sand. Hallelujah. I'm not alone.

I was in Seattle at the University of Washington. It was 1967, and as a member of the medical school faculty I was interested in curricula, helping decide what subjects would be offered. We had just gotten the Rockefeller Foundation grant to establish our division of family planning and human sexuality. At the same time I tried to get a senior medical student included on a panel that was set up to study curricula. The reaction was: What the hell does a student know about curricula? My feeling was: Who knows more?

Now I came full circle, as students became my teachers. Byron Fujita and John Landahl came to my office, telling me they didn't want to fight in Vietnam. (Ned Wagner sent one of them to me.) I suggested they do alternative service with me, assist me in some research projects, and with the draft board's permission that's what they did. Landahl was a biology major and he introduced me to ecology. Fujita was studying psychology, and one day he came in with a book by Carl Rogers and suggested that I read it.

Pretty soon I was reading in the field more heavily than ever before. I asked Ned Wagner for suggestions. Byron Fujita brought in more books. For the first time I was reading people whose ideas were different from those I had been taught when I was in school, concepts that differed from much of what many of my colleagues at the university were then still teaching. These people confirmed what I had come to believe—that education wasn't student-oriented . . . that the health field wasn't patient-oriented or even health-oriented . . . that something was clearly not right.

But it could be fixed. That was the nice part. These people weren't doom-sayers, ranting and raving about things that were "wrong." They were offering a glimpse into the way things could be right.

Carl Rogers was exciting to read. (Well, okay, so he was a little academic, but his *ideas* blew my mind.) He called his patients "clients" in order to meet them on more equal footing—reversing the one-up, one-down relationship of the past. (The patient traditionally looks *up* at the doctor.) He also executed a 180-degree turn away from all previous systems of therapy and left the responsibility for the course and direction of therapy to the client. He talked about how man could learn to have "positive regard" for himself and become "fully functioning."

William Glasser was fighting on the same barricade. He waved a banner marked Reality Therapy, which ignored the client's past, focused on the present and the future, and promoted personal responsibility. "A responsible person," he said, "does that which gives him a feeling of self-worth and a feeling that he is worthwhile to others."

Maxwell Maltz was a man who learned the value of positive self-image as a plastic surgeon and went on to write about emotional face-lifts in *Psycho-Cybernetics*. The secret, he said, was in learning how to make the failure mechanism work for you instead of against you, and acquiring the habit of happiness.

There were dozens more on my reading list and they all were so engagingly positive. I read Norman Allport, one of many voices calling for the study of normal, productive adults as opposed to animals, children, and mental patients; the granddaddy of the self-helpers, Dale Carnegie, whose *How to Win Friends and Influence People* became the largest-selling nonfiction work in the English language, next to the Bible; and the man whose spiritual message pervades the whole humanistic movement, Norman Vincent Peale, whose first book title became a *part* of the English language, *The Power of Positive Thinking*. It was all exciting stuff for me, but no one person turned me on more than someone Werner Erhard mentioned when I took the *est* training in 1973, after coming to Hawaii.

I have to stop for a moment when I introduce Abraham Maslow. I feel a great affection for him—although I never met him; he died in 1970—and happily I give him full credit for a lot of my enthusiasm and much of my style and theory in counseling.

Maslow wrote (in *The Farther Reaches of Human Nature*), "If we want to answer the question how tall can the human species grow, then obviously it is well to pick out the ones who are already tallest and study them. If we want to know how fast a human being can run, then it is no use to average out the speed of a 'good sample' of the population; it is far better to collect Olympic gold medal winners and see how well they can do. If we want to know the possibilities for spiritual growth, value growth, or moral development in human beings, then I maintain that we can learn most by studying our most moral, ethical, or saintly people."

Maslow called these people "self-actualizers," said they were part of society's "growing tip," defined them as individuals who were making the fullest use of their talents, capacities, and potentialities. Maslow believed everyone could attain self-actualization if he or she wished; that this wasn't a utopian dream, but possible under present circumstances.

Maslow believed that people had two kinds of needs—deficiency needs and growth needs. The first of these were the basic needs, needs which, when unfilled, lead to illness and often death. These were the needs for air, water, food, shelter, sleep, sex, safety, and security.

The other kinds of needs were quite different. Maslow said these were what made man godlike. It was natural for man, he said, to need—and seek—loving and belongingness, self-esteem (and esteem by others), meaningfulness, self-sufficiency, effortlessness, playfulness, richness, simplicity, order, justice, completion, necessity, perfection, individuality, aliveness, beauty, goodness, and, at the very peak of his pyramid, truth.

When I first saw this "hierarchy of needs," I was knocked out. Wow, I thought, it's better than the Boy Scout oath. And a heck of a lot more fun.

It literally staggers the mind when you stop and think about it. How many of us still define our psychological self in Freudian terms? How many of us are still living in the same neurotic Oz inhabited by so many of our parents and teachers and clergymen and political leaders? How many of us not only set the very perimeters of our past and present by this same self-defeating yardstick, but also those of our future as well? Isn't it time we all, finally, truly started believing in the post-Freudian revolution that changed all behavioral theory years ago?

Please don't misunderstand me. I'm not saying Freud is without value, or that he has been replaced. The force of his theories is matched only by his brilliance, and his impact will ever be felt. Yet, there is more to the study of human behavior—and its modification—than the study of Freud and his disciples permits. As so many others have pointed out, Freud considered only the "sick" side of psychology—the pathology—and however important that was, by ignoring the "healthy" side of human behavior, there are strong grounds for believing that Freud gave us only half the picture.

Freud developed his theories in Austria just before the turn of the century and up until, say, 1920 or thereabouts. Another well-respected and highly influential man of the period was a German physician named Richard von Krafft-Ebing. He was a professor of medicine at the University of Vienna, and his book, first published in 1886 (in 1922 in the U.S.), *Psychopathia Sexualis,* remains the classic study of sexual pathology—six-hundred-plus pages of pederasty, rape, sexual bondage, sodomy, masochism, sadism, bestiality, necrophilia, nymphomania, satyriasis, incest, lesbianism, homosexuality, and fetishists with fondnesses for hair and shoes and silk and underwear and fur. With Freud's lustful, driving id battling it out with a

highly moralistic superego, and with his obsessions,
phobias, hysteria, paranoiac and hallucinatory psychoses,
it's no wonder that the prevailing sexual attitude came
to resemble a nest of snakes.

I knew it didn't have to be that way. Everywhere I went
I found myself surrounded by people who knew better.

Sexual winners. Who had been losers once.

The best teachers in the field. The very best experts
anywhere.

There was nothing mysterious about what to do with
these winners once they appeared. They could be models
for others.

You see, a teen-ager today who aspires to be a great
football player has successful models aplenty to choose
from and to copy, and if he can't watch his pro and
college heroes in person by attending the games, they
thunder across the television set every autumn weekend—
to be learned from. Someone who wishes to demonstrate
excellence in the kitchen may watch Julia Child and the
Galloping Gourmet and others on TV and take courses at
the local high school, or if he or she lives in London or
Paris or New York, at the Ecole Cordon Bleu. A medical
student can watch great surgeons operate "live" in medical
school amphitheaters or on readily available film and
videotape. Future journalists can learn much from a reading of Bob Woodward and Carl Bernstein's *All the President's Men.* Apprenticeship is available in many forms
today.

But what about the tired sales manager who's just trying
to get it up on Saturday night, and can't? Or the frustrated
mother of three who's never had an orgasm, who's 45 and
wants to redefine her life? Or the inexperienced university
students who wonder why it hurts so much? Or the not-
so-newlyweds who wonder why they've lost interest? Or
all the men who worry about what they label "premature
ejaculation"? Or all the women who want to experience

orgasm vaginally? Who are the successful models for them?

Sexual winners, of course.

My idea was that once I had accumulated enough success stories I could go out there and say to troubled people, "May I assist you with your problem about sexual dissatisfaction?" and they'd say such-and-such and look at me hopefully and I'd say, "Well, I don't know what you want to do about it, but I knew a person once who . . .", and they'd say, "Really? Might it work for me?"

"It might," I'd say. "Go home and try it." And they'd come back and shrug, meaning it didn't work, or smile, meaning the problem was on the way to being eliminated or already was part of the past. If they smiled, I smiled. If they shrugged, I'd say, "I knew another person who . . ."

And the collection of stories I had, by the way, never got used up by any one patient.

Within a few years I gradually became more and more comfortable and adept at assuming a role as an "information (experience) transfer agent"—transferring those experiences from the "successful" to persons who viewed themselves as "unsuccessful." Much to my delight and amazement I began to achieve "success" as a therapist. Soon colleagues began to confer upon me a title of "expert" and called me "the fastest in the West."

Initially my clients were exclusively female—easily explained by the fact that I worked in a woman's clinic. It didn't take very long, however, to discover that sexual problems could be resolved more efficiently by dealing with couples, rather than individual females.

At about this same time I also discovered, quite accidentally, that Dr. William Masters and Mrs. Virginia Johnson were already light-years ahead of where I had so painstakingly arrived.

Alfred Kinsey and his collaborators collected more than 16,000 histories in the 1940s and early 1950s and from this research distilled the world-famous surveys on male and female sexual behavior. More than anything that had come before, these reports dashed on the rocks much of the Victorian morality that had exempted sex from the mainstream of scientific and behavioral research.

And then came the husband-and-wife team of Masters and Johnson, in the late 1960s and early 1970s, taking sex off the drawing board (as their authorized interpreter put it) and into the laboratory, where they proceeded to study the physiology of sex and in due course produce two landmark studies regarding man's and woman's sexual function and dysfunction. There was an added fillip. Where Kinsey merely asked questions and then reported the answers, Masters and Johnson offered suggestions to those with sexual problems and then reported the results of the suggestions. Eventually, Masters and Johnson reported an unprecedented 80 percent "cure rate" among people suffering from various kinds of what they called "sexual inadequacy."

In time my colleagues and I formulated a system which placed the power of change more quickly into the hands of the reader or client. You see, it wasn't all that easy for many people to benefit from what Bill Masters and Virginia Johnson discovered, no matter how much they wished to. To begin with, you had to go to St. Louis. Besides that, the program was open only to couples, and the cost was $2500, and you had to give them two weeks. Any one of these limitations disallowed thousands. In combination, nearly everyone was eliminated. It was too far to go, it cost too much, and it required a greater time investment than was reasonable for most people. The program was excellent, and it served as many as Masters and Johnson could possibly shoehorn into a rapidly constricting personal schedule, and unavoidably there were thousands left on the outside looking in.

Bill and Virginia Masters allowed many of us, subsequently, to climb upon their shoulders, and in so doing, I saw a terrain somewhat different from that described by them and I found a path easier to follow than the one that they suggested.

CHAPTER

3

The Top Ten Sexual Complaints

I remember a popular slogan from the 1960s: "I Am a Human Being—Do Not Fold, Spindle, or Mutilate." About the same time this appeared on bumper stickers and lapel buttons, Bob Dylan wrote a song, "All I Really Want to Do," in which he decried society's tendency to simplify and classify everything and everyone.

I hate labels today as much as Bob Dylan did ten years ago. I believe that the process of classifying those seeking assistance seems wasteful of time and energy and may be experienced as demeaning.

For example, Harvey Petersen came to me complaining of "premature ejaculation." I asked him what he meant.

"Well," he said, "I come in four minutes and I read in one of those books that the average guy lasts *seven* minutes."

We talked some more, and in time I found out that his wife usually experienced orgasm in three minutes, a full minute before he did. Yet by somebody's definition he was a "premature ejaculator."

Look at it another way: Has any male "prematurely ejaculated" during masturbation?

You see what I mean? I don't know what the label means.

The same thing happens when you talk about "impotence." Bill Sanchez can't get it up for his wife, but sometimes wakes up in the morning hard.

With *his* wife, Mike Green sometimes can and sometimes can't; he calls his penis "Old Unreliable." While Peter Costello complains of sometimes getting only partially hard.

Who's "impotent" and who isn't in this group? And what does "impotent" mean?

Beverly Sanders shares a common female complaint with thousands of others—she has not experienced orgasm. Her husband calls her "frigid." Is she?

What, then, of Teri Tremaine, who is bored, who turns completely off when her husband of ten years comes near her or touches her? Is this the definition of "frigidity"?

How about Alison McConnell, who has never experienced orgasm with her partner, but does through masturbation? Is she "frigid"?

And what of Penny Miyake, who is suffering from dyspareunia (pain during intercourse) and makes up excuses to avoid contact with her husband? Is *she* "frigid"?

A woman who wants her husband to pay more attention to her, and more often, is called a "nympho." A man who wants it "all the time" is called a "sex maniac" or a "stud," depending on the point of view. Disinterested and inexperienced women are called "cold fish" and "lousy lays." A man with an orgasm problem is called a "quick trigger." The labels go on and on and on. All are demeaning, all are counterproductive, all are confusing.

So, everyone's problem is unique.

But.

There *are* similarities. A review of the psychological and therapeutic literature and my own years in practice provide ample evidence that there are areas of commonality, proof that no one is really all alone. In other words, there are certain complaints which we hear most often, and it appears to me that these Top 'len Sexual Complaints fall generally into three areas of sexual dissatisfaction: (1) Desire, (2) Arousal, and (3) Orgasm.

PROBLEMS OF DESIRE

These are the problems of longingness and regretfulness and wishfulness and cravingness. These are the problems of absence. There is something *missing*.

Problem No. 1: "I Don't Want to Do It."

(Putting this problem first, by the way, does not mean it is the most common problem, only that it is the first in this brief introduction.)

Buffy thinks sex is awful. It hurt the first time and she got pregnant besides, and she married him. Now she is sickened by the sight of her husband unclothed. She abhors bodily contact, says talk about sex "repulses me, stops me cold." She wonders if the neighbors can hear and if the children might wake up. Afterward, she is anxious to get into the bathroom to "clean up." Not long ago she bought *The Joy of Sex*, thinking it might help, and she "got sick to my stomach looking at the pictures." She admits this is "silly," considering she has two children, but she feels this way nonetheless. She says, in words I've heard so often they are almost a sexual cliché, "Almost every day I'm wondering in my mind if I'm going to have to go through it that night."

When Jack and Sally were living together before they

married, they were making love four and five times a week. That was seven years ago, and now the incidence has dropped to maybe once a month. Sex is a hassle for Jack—when he's ready, his wife isn't, and when she's ready, he's not. He believes that "my wife is not that sexually attractive to me anymore; there are times when we do have sex and I do enjoy having sex and being physically intimate with her, but I find myself not sexually aroused by her body most of the time." He says it's gotten so he'd rather masturbate, and he usually feels terribly guilty about that.

Both these individuals, Buffy and Jack, have their very unique problems, but they are saying the same thing: "I don't feel like doing it (with my partner)."

Problem No. 2: "I Want to Do It More."

Here's another classic. Richard said, "My wife and I love each other. We enjoy each other's company, we enjoy each other's conversation. I find her a very stimulating person with whom to exchange ideas. She's an excellent hostess. She has all the attributes of a perfect wife except that she is not the passionate witch that I would like to have around at times." Richard was "uptight about the fact that I always have to make the overtures." In order to "wear off this sex drive" he had taken up horseback riding and tennis and had, at her suggestion, taken cold showers regularly. He was masturbating more often than he was sharing sex with his wife when he came to see me, and was contemplating having an affair. The only thing unusual about Richard is that most men I've met with his complaint already have had an affair, or several.

Patti was nearing 40 and had experienced no slack in her sexual appetite, but her husband's eye had long wandered elsewhere, and now she was left at home with every appliance in the world, the kids nearly grown, and a wishywashyness about her future that left her with the willies. When she found out Terry was cheating on her, she picked up a man in a bar to get even. That was six years ago. Now she was thinking about looking around for "something serious—someone who'll tell me I'm still pretty and let me know I'm really needed." She told me about the years when she and her mate made love almost every day. She said she wished she could roll the calendar back. "A woman gets horny, too," she said.

Both these individuals, Richard and Patti, are saying, "I feel like doing it more often (all the time), but my partner doesn't."

Problem No. 3: "We Don't Do It Anymore."

Malcolm and Nancy married in their thirties, and were nearly sixty when the last child left home. That was five years ago, and now, approaching retirement age, they were worrying about how much future they have left and wondering what they might do with it. They hadn't shared a bed in seven years. Malcolm figured it was because he gave so much of himself to his successful insurance business: "At first I said I didn't have time and then I realized I didn't have any interest either." For years Nancy had contented herself with running the house and doing volunteer secretarial work at a local drug rehabilitation halfway house. They shared many intimacies, but never sex.

Tom and Tamara, who are only in their late twenties, got it down to *her* birthday, *his* birthday, and New Year's Eve—the rest of the year (for the past two years) had been barren. "When it becomes ritualistic," she said, "it's already nonexistent. It's like painting by the numbers—nobody's ever going to call that art." She blamed him, said he never outgrew a playboy adolescence that made him an incorrigible skirt-chaser. He said she wasn't feminine enough for him, especially since she had quit her job as a stewardess and joined a women's consciousness-raising group. They both claimed to be in love with each other, and didn't know what to do about it.

Malcolm and Nancy and Tom and Tamara are bored. And none of them know what to do about it.

"I don't want to do it."
"I want to do it more."
"We don't do it anymore."

The three most common complaints in Desire are the problems of boredom and turning off.

He wants it, she doesn't.

Or she wants it and he doesn't.

Or neither one of them wants it.

The rhythms are wrong. Excuses are made. Lies are told. Frustration and anger result. It is almost as if we were following scripts. In fact, Eric Berne, the author of *Games People Play* and the father of transactional analysis, says that's what we do—follow "scripts." Werner Erhard says in his Erhard Seminars Training (*est*) that we go through life "running our tapes" much as if we were Barbie Dolls with strings in our necks.

We have gone on automatic pilot. We do that whenever we are not celebrating. Of course it is fantastic when it serves you. I think automatic pilot is great. It lets me think about something while I'm getting dressed or carry on a conversation while driving a car. But most of the time automatic pilot doesn't serve anybody as much as it could.

For example, Ted and Marcia have stopped talking in bed. He does what worked. She does what worked. But they are not checking to see if it *still* works, and they are making an effort, and they are on automatic pilot because they remembered that this is what they always liked. Only now she is saying to herself, "I don't like that anymore" or "Can't he think of anything else?" And *he's* thinking, "How come she's not doing what she always does at this point?"

Some people seem to think that if it worked once, it'll work again. That's not true with human beings, only with white mice and other laboratory animals.

Other people seem to have stopped thinking. And feeling. And doing. Desire is missing.

PROBLEMS OF AROUSAL

Problems of arousal occur when the person possibly thinks desire but fails to awaken or stir from inactivity. There is no real excitation. This is a region rich in therapeutics, one which bears two of the most frightening labels, *impotence* and *dyspareunia*.

Problem No. 4: "I Can't Get It Up."

Carlos experienced no difficulty getting an erection during a four-year marriage. Nor did he have any problems in a long, intimate relationship that followed. Then came a period of one-nighters and weekenders, when he noticed that "I wasn't able to perform," which caused him to end the relationship quickly, only to begin another. This pattern of dating was broken when Carlos met a woman he wished to marry. Unfortunately he still was unable to get an erection most of the time. She wanted to marry him anyway, and he wanted to be able to "give her the normal sex life that she's entitled to."

Buddy had had two sexually successful extramarital

affairs when he came to me, but he reported he couldn't get an erection for his wife. A conversation with Stella revealed she had threatened Buddy with separation and divorce, she had thrown tantrums and gone on crying spells. She admitted that she had created "some terrible scenes . . . very bitter, very ugly things," and said he had "ignored my emotional needs." He said he thought it was the children who kept them together.

Only 5 percent of all erection problems are organic. These people will never, ever have an erection again, unless they have one of those hydraulic operations, where a mechanical apparatus is inserted surgically and subsequently the penis is inflated like a beach toy. William was a diabetic, for example; Mel was burned-out (reformed) alcoholic; and Sandy had prostate cancer.

Problem No. 5: "I Can't Keep It Up" or "It's Too Soft."

Robert was really just one step away from "I don't want to do it" (Problem No. 1). Sex with his wife of 12 years no longer really turned him on, the creativity that defined their early relationship was worn out, or was being ignored. He still loved his wife, or said he did, and out of duty as much as anything else, managed to effect an erection a perfunctory once or twice a week. Invariably he would lose it shortly after intercourse began. He said, "That's the way it always is—my mind wanders."

My colleague Jack Annon, in his book *The Behavioral Treatment of Sexual Prolems,* reported a case where a man learned while in a boy's school how to masturbate to ejaculation without getting an erection. There are others who seem only partly aroused; it is as if the physical stimulation (manual or oral) were causing minimal wetness or penile engorgement, but never enough to effect true arousal. After a while the mind turned the arousal switch off.

Problem No. 6: "It Hurts."

For a while Sandra blamed the pain she felt during intercourse on vaginal injuries sustained in an automobile accident. Now she is questioning her marriage of eight years to Danny. For most of that time she says, "I pretended that I enjoyed it." She "always thought sex would be a certain way and it just wasn't." She wonders if she still loves her husband. At the same time, she feels guilty when she fantasizes sex with another man. She says she hates sex with Danny because of the pain, and wonders if it wasn't really the other way around—first she disliked sex with Danny, *then* she got the pain to justify infrequent sex.

Sandra is experiencing dyspareunia, doctor talk for painful intercourse. So is Louann, who has a bacterial infection. And so is Penny, who fails to lubricate, which actually indicates a failure to be sexually aroused.

Sometimes dyspareunia leads to the next common complaint.

Problem No. 7: "We Can't Do It."

Debbi was the oldest of nine children and by the time she was 12 years old, she was virtually raising them. (Her father was hospitalized, her mother worked two jobs.) Although she has been attempting sexual intercourse for nine years (she is 27) and has been married for five to a man who says he has a "large sexual appetite," penile penetration has never been accomplished. Whenever her husband Eddie tries it, she "freezes up" and penetration becomes physically impossible. She wants to go off the birth control pill and get a tubal ligation. He says he may wish to have a child some day and forbids her to have such an operation.

Mary was a classic, showing many of the most common characteristics. She was raised in Kentucky by grandparents who provided a restrictive religious environment. She was raped at 14 by an uncle. She had never "consummated" her marriage of one year to Ben and she noticed that he was then beginning to experience an erection problem.

Debbi and Mary have vaginismus.

I don't use labels like impotence and dyspareunia to describe people like Carlos and Buddy and Robert and Sandra and Debbi and Mary. I recognize them as problems of arousal. When the penis doesn't erect or wilts and the vagina doesn't lubricate, when it hurts, it never is much fun. The desire may be there, then something always, uh, peters out and the well runs dry. You are not turned on.

PROBLEMS OF ORGASM

Here are the complaints that sometimes come even if you *are* turned on. They concern the speed with which one reaches the orgasmic state, or the seeming inability to experience it at all. This category includes the two most common complaints of all.

Problem No. 8: "I Come Too Fast."

Paul's earliest sexual experiences were in an automobile, in a hurry. Later he was serious about a woman who felt guilty about "doing it" unmarried, so required a lot of "persuasion" before she'd go to bed with him. He was married when he came to my office and said he was "incapable of withholding my climax long enough to bring my wife to a climax through intercourse." Recently he had used oral and manual manipulation to bring on his wife's orgasm and figured that that was the best there was under the existing circumstances. Then she expressed a total lack of interest.

Andy has been (his words) a "quick trigger" since he married, and they have consoled themselves that things would change after they got accustomed to married life. But nothing did change and Betty began to think of herself as a receptacle. Andy has tried biting his lip, thinking of garbage, and multiplying seven times seven times seven endlessly, to take his mind away from what he is feeling; he has worn extra-thick condoms, has even pulled hair from his legs. He is beginning to doubt his masculinity and she is losing confidence in herself as a woman.

Problem No. 9: "I Can't Come at All."

Her husband was surprised when after a year of marriage Barbara said she'd never experienced an orgasm with him. She explained, "I'm a pretty good actress." Now she wished she'd kept her mouth shut because the relationship has gone straight downhill. She said they didn't even seem to have anything much in common anymore. He was a night person and she folded up by 8 or 9 P.M. They also both kept themselves busy with civic meetings, night school, and charity work, so that they seldom really spent much time together. Of course by now sex was a no-no, with Barbara doing everything possible to avoid it. At the same time, she fantasized orgasms all day long.

Theresa had failed to experience orgasm so many times, as she put it, "I almost hate to try again, I don't want the disappointment." She had taken her problem to eight counselors and psychiatrists and once, with her husband's permission, she slept with another man to see if the problem possibly was her husband's rather than her own. She still didn't come.

Problem No. 10: "I Can't Come During Intercourse."

Eva found it fairly simple to reach an orgasm using a vibrator and, with her husband of nine years, orally and manually, but not with him "during intercourse." It was a problem, she said, that was affecting her "attitudes about everything—my attitude about myself especially."

Melinda reported orgasming twice while petting as a teenager, and later with a vibrator regularly, but never during a marriage that recently broke up and never with the partners she'd dated since.

I suppose there is still one more common complaint in the orgasm category. That is, "We can't come together." This is very common. The truth is, I don't think this is grounds for complaint. I believe it is possibly an unsuitable goal.

The comedian Allan Sherman called it "The Magic Fuck," and he didn't think there was anything magical about it either. I don't even think it's advisable. I mean, it's an okay thing to experience when it happens. But, really, it's like sneezing at the same time with someone and then attaching significance to it.

When two people set simultaneous orgasm as their goal and use this shared explosion as the yardstick against which they measure all sexual experience, they deny themselves much freedom and much pleasure, while programming themselves for disappointment in some or most of their sexual encounters.

Simultaneous orgasm is supposed to be the ultimate in positive sharing, but actually it is the opposite, because when the male is climaxing, he is not thinking of anyone other than himself, he is not thinking of anything other than his own orgasm. And when the female climaxes, she assumes the same natural but selfish posture and experiences only *her* orgasm, thinks only of herself. They have shared timing, but who knows how much else.

Even worse is how setting this goal can actually make the most natural act in the world difficult. Coming together is usually making it the difficult way, and I don't know that making it that way is better. Picture a couple in bed, determined to reach orgasm at the same instant. They've been at it for awhile now and he feels ejaculation approaching.

"Now? Now? Now?" he asks.

She answers, "Not yet, keep going, keep going."

Soon he is huffing and puffing and possibly biting his lip or multiplying seven times seven times seven. "Now?" he says. "Please, now?"

"Not yet, not yet, soon."

"Hurry, I can't wait, I'm . . ."

"Wait, wait, no, oh, wait, wait . . ."

There is a long silence. He is still. Finally he says quietly, ashamedly, "I'm sorry, honey, but . . ."

I'm sorry, too. It doesn't have to be that way.

EVERYBODY'S NORMAL

These are the most often heard complaints in any sex counselor's office. Do any of them sound familiar? Please be aware that you are probably a little bit odd if at least one of them doesn't. It is "normal" to feel and think and do good in sex, but it is also "normal" to not feel, think, and perform so well.

Remember in eighth-grade biology when we learned about the "normal" bell curve? (See page 35.) Over there on the left and right were the extremists, the ones with the radical or unusual points of view. That was where the fewest people were. Most of the people were in the middle. That's what gave the curve its bell shape. The point is, no matter what you felt, or thought, or did, you were somewhere on the "normal" curve.

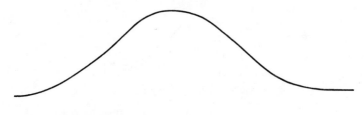

Besides being "normal," it's also okay to be where you are, to have zero to minus-ten sex. Unless, of course, you or someone else gets hurt. It's good to be responsible, and I think being responsible is fulfilling your own wants and needs whatever they may be and noticing that you're not preventing someone else from fulfilling his or her own wants and needs.

Assuming this responsibility, everyone might notice that there is nothing *wrong* with being the way we are—if our problems are not hurting anyone else, or ourselves, and if that's the way we want to be.

We are perfect as we are, and it's okay if we want to stay that way, and it's okay if we want to change. It's our choice.

DESIRE, AROUSAL, ORGASM: THE CYCLE OF LIFE

Desire, arousal, and orgasm define the cycle of all of life's experiences, not just its sexual response cycle.

You see, I understand that desire is basically the same thing as thought. Desire has to do with the cognitive processes, the thinking we do. When you form the words

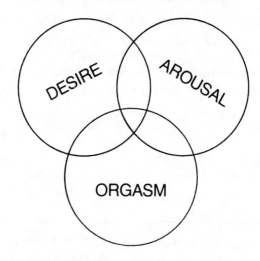

aloud or in your head, "I want her (him)," you may *feel* something; perhaps you wet your lips with your tongue or begin to breathe more heavily. But your primary activity is thinking. Desire is no longer primitive. Now we react to each other according to how we learned to react. There are certain types and certain conditions that turn us on, and these are learned. The intellectual processes are at work, pulling all the strings or not pulling them.

Arousal has more to do with what psychologists call affective behavior, that which centers on the emotions, or feelings. Again there is overlap. To be aroused (once noticed) is already to have desiring (thinking) behavior. It also includes doing behaviors, like when you experience erection or wetness. But once again there is a primary kind of behavior, and that is feeling. It is beyond being inspired and not quite into full-out action. It is getting really, *really* turned on.

And orgasm relates to motor (doing) behavior. This is action central, where, as the surfers say, you "go for it." There is no turning back. Commitment, which has been building in steps one and two, desire and arousal, is now as complete as it's going to get. It is very physical.

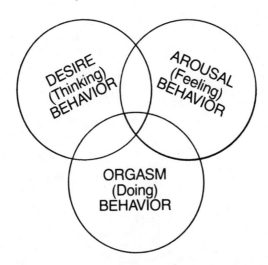

Still another way of looking at the cycle is to consider desire as being related to what most people call "motivation"; I call it "readiness," being with purpose and full of hope. It's being ready to get off the dime and knowing where you want to go, and believing you can get there.

Whereas arousal may be equated with "participation." This is actually getting off the dime. There is involvement. The *Oxford English Dictionary* defines "participation" as "the fact or condition of sharing in common." You are no longer alone, you are *with*.

Orgasm by definition is "intense excitement," and that completes the cycle. Intense excitement is the "thanks" we get for our commitment, the "reward" or resolution that comes at the end of any cycle. This is where nearly everyone wishes to be—having one of Maslow's "peak experiences."

Desire, arousal, orgasm.

How an individual rates his or her experience of any of these three areas determines to a great extent whether the cycle continues, and what excitement it continues with. And if completed, when it might begin again.

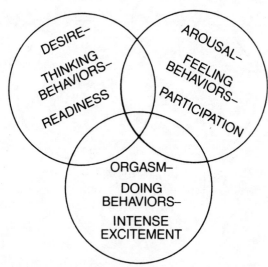

If the cycle is not completed, or is completed with only minimal satisfaction, it means you are stuck. It is like a washing machine being stuck midcycle, at "rinse" or possibly "spin."

Getting Stuck in Desire

Buffy, who was repulsed by the sight of her husband's naked body and worried whether or not she will have to "go through with it that night," was stuck in desire; she had none. So was Jack, who made love with his wife four or five times weekly seven years before, but now said he would rather masturbate. Richard's wife told him to take cold showers when he wanted intimacy. Patti's husband was cheating on her and she was being ignored. Malcolm and Nancy hadn't shared sex in seven years.

Getting stuck in desire was saying:

"I don't want to do it."

"I want to do it more."

"We don't do it anymore."

Getting stuck in desire may mean you never reach the

cycle's second and third stages, and if you do, the pleasure is diminished; one's potential is crippled. How is it possible to enjoy sex when you really don't want to have anything to do with it?

Getting Stuck in Arousal

Carlos had plenty of desire for his wife-to-be, but he was unable to count on getting an erection. Buddy believed it was the children who kept the marriage together and got erections only for his extramarital affairs. Robert, on the other hand, gets an erection, but can't keep it. Sandra said it hurt, and Debbi and Mary said they were so tight it wasn't possible.

Getting stuck in arousal was saying:

"*I can't get it up.*"

"*I can't keep it up.*" (Or: "*It's too soft.*")

"*It hurts.*"

"*We can't do it.*"

Getting stuck in arousal is getting part of the way there, but it means you may never reach the final stage, or it may severely undercut the enjoyment of that stage. This is the area of the greatest pain, disappointment, and frustration. How is it possible to enjoy sex when you want to and don't think you can?

Getting Stuck in Orgasm

Paul and Andy were self-proclaimed "quick triggers," and Barbara, Theresa, and Emily had failed time after time to experience orgasm or to experience it vaginally with their partners.

Getting stuck in orgasm was saying:

"*I come too fast.*"

"*I can't come.*"

"*I can't come vaginally.*"

Getting stuck in orgasm was getting most of the way and then "failing." Repeated failure in this stage of the cycle often results in a failure to start the cycle again. In this way, men and women sometimes find themselves stuck in more than one stage at the same time. It is not unusual, for example, for the husband of a nonorgasmic woman to experience such guilt that he loses interest in his wife sexually and then actually loses his ability to get or sustain an erection as well. Now the man and woman are sharing not intimacy but "stuckness."

Where Are You on the Stuckness Scale?

Let the following be a scale of sexual *desire*. Where do you think you fit at present?

| Minimal Desire | 0 1 2 3 4 5 6 7 8 9 10 | Maximal Desire |

Let the following be a scale of sexual *arousal* (without orgasm). In the past, practicing self-stimulation (masturbation), you have experienced

| Minimal Arousal | 0 1 2 3 4 5 6 7 8 9 10 | Maximal **Arousal** |

In the past, with a partner you have experienced

| Minimal Arousal | 0 1 2 3 4 5 6 7 8 9 10 | Maximal **Arousal** |

Let the following be a scale of sexual *orgasm*. In the past while practicing self-stimulation, your orgasms have been of

| Minimal Intensity | 0 1 2 3 4 5 6 7 8 9 10 | Maximal Intensity |

In the past, with a partner your orgasms have been of

| Minimal Intensity | 0 1 2 3 4 5 6 7 8 9 10 | Maximal Intensity |

Let the following be a scale of *satisfaction* after sexual activity. In the past, practicing self-stimulation you have experienced

| Minimal
Satisfaction | 0 | 1 | 2 | 3 | 4 | 5 | 6 | 7 | 8 | 9 | 10 | Maximal
Satisfaction |

In the past, with a partner you have experienced

| Minimal
Satisfaction | 0 | 1 | 2 | 3 | 4 | 5 | 6 | 7 | 8 | 9 | 10 | Maximal
Satisfaction |

Looking into the future, note on the scale where you would like to be in regard to

DESIRE	Minimal Desire	0	1	2	3	4	5	6	7	8	9	10	Maximal Desire
AROUSAL	Minimal Arousal	0	1	2	3	4	5	6	7	8	9	10	Maximal Arousal
ORGASM	Minimal Orgasm	0	1	2	3	4	5	6	7	8	9	10	Maximal Orgasm
SATISFACTION	Minimal Satisfaction	0	1	2	3	4	5	6	7	8	9	10	Maximal Satisfaction

CHAPTER

4

The Rating Game

Picture a graph shaped like half a pizza with minus ten at the left, plus ten at the right, and zero in the middle. This scale can be used by an individual or couple to evaluate (rate, score, judge, quantify) an ongoing or a recently concluded sexual experience.

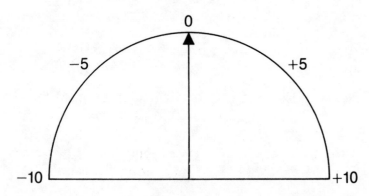

Many people are unaware of their self-ratings or their "other-ratings" (how other people look at them). It is important for those anxious to change their behavior to be made aware of this scoring system so that it may be used to enhance the quality of a relationship.

And how might that be done? Well, once people are clear as to where on a spectrum of minus ten to plus ten they fit, an opportunity to choose a different location is presented. Any journey begins at a starting point, and knowing where you are starting from makes it possible to get where you want to go.

Look at the scale for a moment. Think of it as representing the vast and varied panorama of all human sexual experience—past, present, and fantasied future. On the left, or zero-to-minus-ten side are the ten most common complaints (and hundreds more as well). This is where sexual "losers" hang out. This is the half of the scale where dissatisfaction and dysfunction reign. This is the underside of sexuality that has been so thoroughly probed and reported by Freud, Krafft-Ebing, Masters and Johnson, Stoller, and so many more. I call it Leftsidedness.

On the right, or zero-to-plus-ten side of the scale you find the opposite. Here are the sexual "winners," those who have found satisfaction. This is the side of wellness, an expanded model of health. I call *this* Rightsidedness.

Zero represents exactly what it means: neutrality, emptiness, the absence of everything. Boredom plus. It is a handy dividing point, but nothing more. It is not a barrier separating Leftsidedness from Rightsidedness. How could it be? It is nothing.

What sort of separation, or barrier, is there, then? There are many, of course, and one of the biggest is us, the so-called health profession, which is really a disease profession, as I learned during my medical school training and residency. We doctors (and nurses and psychiatrists and psychologists and so on) know all about people in the zero-to-minus-ten area, but we have spent precious little time and effort looking at the zero-to-plus-ten sector. We know all about diagnosing and retarding and curing and even preventing disease, but we cannot describe clearly what "wellness" is, or even could be. It's fuzzy—lacking solidity.

By the age of six, for example, every child can tell you what a headache is, especially if there's a television set in the home. But how many of these youngsters can describe a "headpleasure"?

Can you describe a headpleasure? Can I?

How about a backpleasure? Or a toothpleasure? Or a bellypleasure? Or a loose neck? Or blissing feet?

People sometimes smile indulgently when I use these strange new words and phrases. Then I explain about Leftsidedness and Rightsidedness. Pretty soon they are asking shyly, "Do you know what a headpleasure is?"

And I say, "I knew someone once . . ."

LEFT BEHIND, LEFT OVER, LEFT OUT

Being Leftsided is emphasizing one's liabilities, letting them get in the way of assets, or forgetting assets altogether. For example, many men complaining of intermittent erection problems (and the problems usually are getting worse) tell me that when they find themselves in bed with a desirable partner, they remember only the recent failures to erect, not the recent successes. This memory triggers the fear of repeated failure, the fear of repeated failure causes anxiety, and anxiety may result in —you guessed it—another failure.

Being Leftsided is being stuck in the past or the present, unaware of the future. It is being concerned only with what sex used to be or is, as opposed to what sex *could* be. It is women who have never experienced orgasm believing they never will.

Being Leftsided is making excuses and finding people to blame instead of being responsible. How many thousands of men and women have postponed sex by saying they were tired, or by reminding each other that the children were still awake, or complaining of a headache? (To think that a headpleasure is her or his alternative!) How many thousands more blame their mothers or fathers or partners for current problems?

Being Leftsided is turning off instead of turning on. I always ask my clients what they have done about the problem before coming to me, and nearly every last one of them has mentioned a period of not doing anything. They figured if they ignored the problem, one day it would disappear.

Being Leftsided is hanging out with a lot of strong negative feelings about sex. It is being disgusted and embarrassed and tense, and feeling shame, aggression, guilt, anger, selfishness, possessiveness, resentment, fear, frustration, irritation, discomfort, insecurity, deceit, and pain.

BROKEN BODIES, BROKEN MINDS, AND BROKEN HEARTS

After saying all that, I now say this: There is nothing wrong with being Leftsided.

I just want you to notice that it's rich in therapeutic value, that it's a place where doctors and nurses and psychiatrists and others in the health-support system offer valued assistance in moving from illness to the absence of illness. There always will be a need for therapeutics—from first aid to surgery to intensive therapy—because there always will be broken bodies, broken minds, and broken hearts.

Nowhere do I want to make zero to minus ten wrong. Left is okay. It is as valid as Right. It is in no way worse than Right, or less than Right. It's just different.

The thing is, I notice there are a lot of people who wish to change sides. And celebrate.

Even Carl Jung, who seemed Leftsided at times (along with his colleague Freud), said, "I prefer to understand man in the perspective of his health." And Alfred Adler followed him with the belief that overcoming weakness (or disadvantage) was no less than the driving force of mankind; the "great upward drive" he called it. Abraham Maslow's "self-actualizers," Carl Rogers' "fully functioning man," Erich Fromm's "productive man"—there was great agreement, it was all part of an upward and forward thrust that commands our attention today.

Just as being Leftsided was entertaining strong negative feelings, being Rightsided is experiencing strong positive feelings, such as generosity, security, grace, wholeness, perfection, fairness, richness, uniqueness, pleasure, gratification, fulfillment, ease, contentment, exhilaration, confidence, delight, relaxation, peacefulness, excitement, honesty, freedom, sensuality, creativity, imagination, union, and joy. The list goes on and on and on.

It is as if we have suddenly rediscovered the meaning of the word "health," returning to the Anglo-Saxon root meaning "whole." "Heal" comes from the same root, as does "holy." The notion of health as wholeness, as the mind and spirit and body (thinking, feeling, and doing) is not new, but it is new for our times.

Until recently, the right side of our Rating Game scale, the zero-to-plus-ten sector of human sexuality, was an

unknown region which lay like the Hawaiian Islands before Captain Cook in 1778, or before the Polynesian chiefs
hundreds of years before that—a garden of uncharted wonder. Only now the significance and advantage of Rightsidedness is becoming clear, as those who are now
Rightsided emerge as models and teachers for those who
wish to change sides.

Rightsidedness, eh? And what in the world is that?

It resides in your other brain.

My other brain? you ask.

Of course. The other one. The one on the right side of
your head.

INTO THE ENCHANTED LOOM

A poet once described the brain as "that enchanted loom
where millions of flashing shuttles weave a dissolving
pattern."

How terrific that is. How perfectly it captures the
mystery and lure, while it embraces the thousands of
questions we have, for brain research today is in a primitive state. The truth is, we really don't know very much
about how it works. However, among the things we do
know is that there are, in a way, not one but two brains—
a right and a left hemisphere.

Hold it! you say? Two halves don't make two brains.

True enough. But listen.

Place your hands on your head, positioning your right
thumb over your right ear, your left thumb over your
left ear, elbows close together, fingers of both hands beginning to touch over the rear or crown of the skull. Notice
the area covered by each hand. Your left hand is covering,
or rather cradling, the left side of the brain, and your right
hand is covering the right side.

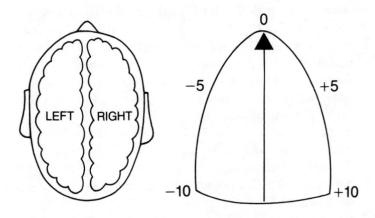

Each side, or hemisphere, governs half the body—the left brain receiving and sending and affecting messages to the right arm and leg and fingers and toes, the right hemisphere doing the same for the left side of the body. Although many of the duties of both sides are similar, a study of persons with brain damage to one side or the other has shown that each half seems to have certain specialized responsibilities. These functions are so different (yet complementary of course) that science now talks about the Logical (Left) Brain and the Artistic (Right) Brain.

A perfect example of this was reported in *Psychology Today*:

> Managers feel that planners are too remote from the hurly-burly of everyday business to develop a workable long-range strategy. Planners, in turn, see their best-laid plans sabotaged by managers who seem to make decisions on the fly, without sufficient analysis.
>
> Management-researcher Henry Mintzberg of Mc-Gill University believes that these conflicts are more

than a matter of different viewpoints or personalities. They reflect basic differences in thinking, differences which are based on which side of the person's brain is better developed. Managers work best with their right hemisphere; planners use the left hemisphere more effectively.

Neurologists, psychologists, and other researchers have learned that the two hemispheres are specialized in fundamental ways. Logical thinking takes place in the left hemisphere (except for some left-handed persons), while the right hemisphere handles broader, relational functions. The left side works in linear fashion, processing information sequentially; language is a left-hemisphere function. The right side specializes in simultaneous processing of information; handling spatial relationships is one of its jobs.

These differences in hemispheric function—sequential and analytical vs. simultaneous and impressionistic—parallel the different skills required by planners and managers. Obviously the split isn't complete. Planners use some intuition to do their jobs properly and managers must be able to implement their decisions in orderly ways. But the essential skills are different.*

The Rightsided managers Mintzberg surveyed preferred meetings over memos in order to study facial expressions, mental impressions, and other speculative information. They talked about an ability to get "the big picture" and follow "hunches." This is the sort of "soft" information processed most efficiently by the right brain.

The division of responsibilities, then, is:

* From "Good Managers Rely on Their Right Brains," by Jack Horn. Reprinted from *Psychology Today* magazine. Copyright © 1976 Ziff-Davis Publishing Company.

Logical (Left)	Artistic (Right)
Complex use of words	Simple use of words
Difficult calculation	Simple arithmetic
Language; the expression of verbal ideas	Images; the expression of nonverbal ideas; spatial orientation
Processing information sequentially	Simultaneous processing of varied information
Logic, the ability to analyze	Intuition
Mental talents	Artistic talents

Anthropologists and psychologists now believe that entire civilizations have developed under the influence of the hemisphere that was dominant in the population. It's further believed that Western society is one of those dominated by the left or logical brain. This is reflected in the design and values of this culture.

For example, when I was in high school, there were basically two kinds of curricula—one that ostensibly prepared you for college and one that did not. The college preparatory course was jammed full of classes in algebra, history, and English literature—subjects that relied upon the Left Brain. Meanwhile, those *not* headed for another four years of schooling took secretarial courses (typing, shorthand, etc.), or classes in woodworking (shop) or home economics (cooking). I recall how many in college prep classes looked down their noses at those majoring in home ec or shop, considered them mentally and socially inferior. Being Leftsided in those days seemed to be the best way to be.

Another example emerges from the quickest look at the way Western man (and woman) earns a living. Persons with Leftsided jobs, such as lawyers, stockbrokers, doctors, accountants, and scientists, usually are paid exceptionally well and enjoy high social status.

Most of the Rightsided artists, musicians, and poets are poorly paid or not paid at all. The unspoken philosophy summed up in the cliché "starving artist" tells just how Leftsided Western society is.

Mintzberg described his Rightsided manager as being "involved, plugged in, his mode of operating is relational, simultaneous, experiential"; yet, he added, management schools along with the rest of society have done everything possible to squelch this line of thought, leaving the essential Rightsided part of management to sneak in the backdoor, unobserved and largely unappreciated.

Why have we done this? Why have we neglected to show the right side the recognition it deserves? Why have we failed to nurture it? Why have we labeled it so unkindly? "Starving artist," indeed. Why have we starved our Artistic Brain?

Whatever the reason—and these questions obviously deserve more study—we find ourselves, in the seventies, generally stuck in Leftsidedness. Why? Because in growing up in our society that's the way we learned to be.

Of course it needn't remain this way. The choice is ours. If we choose, we may now give Rightsidedness that which it commands—our attention. Now we may explore that part of ourselves that we have kept in the behavioral closet all these years. Now the represssed artist or appreciator of art that is in so many of us may surface. Now imagination and fantasy may open new vistas. Now we may be clear that there is much, much more to life than we always thought there was, and go after it. If we choose to.

You see, as long as we're familiar with both the right and left sides, we can complete ourselves—we can have a self-self relationship. That means you know who you are, you've stopped hiding secrets even from yourself, and you like yourself, totally. Everything works. You are perfectly balanced, without conflict.

Figure how that would relate to, and change, your position on the minus-ten-to-plus-ten scale of sex.

Far out, right?

COUNTING SIGHS, NOT SIZE

Whenever I talk about zero-to-plus-ten sex, someone inevitably asks, "I can imagine zero to, say, plus five or six, or maybe even seven, but tell me, what's the ultimate? What *is* plus-ten sex?"

My colleague in Honolulu, Jack Annon, tells of a man who complained of "premature ejaculation." Annon asked him what he meant by that.

"Well," he said, "my wife and I usually engage in petting for maybe ten minutes or so, and then I enter her and after about two or three minutes, I come."

Two or three minutes isn't too far from average, but Annon didn't interrupt. The man continued his story.

"Well, we might change positions, and then I continue for another ten minutes or so, and I come a second time. Somewhere around here, as I continue, she usually comes, too, but it takes me another twenty or twenty-five minutes before I come again. And the fourth time for me usually takes another half hour to forty-five minutes."

The average reader may by now wonder just what this man's problem was. The man apparently was able to sustain an erection for an hour and a half (on and off) while experiencing four orgasms—what possibly could be wrong? Well, as it turned out, he said he was having trouble in recent weeks reaching the fourth orgasm; could therapy make it "the way it was"?

Was this man's performance "plus-ten sex"?

And what about one of my own clients, a woman who told me that the first time she was sexually satisfied, she was alone and had 50 orgasms without even using her hands.

Was this plus-ten sex?

For me, plus-ten sex has nothing whatsoever to do with supernormal powers—"supernormal" being that which gets to be defined sometimes as if normal people come once, then supernormal people come five times—or in the above cases, four and 50 times.

That's measurement rather than qualitative exploration. That's not measuring sighs, it's measuring size.

I want to be very clear about this. There are people who truly get stuck in measuring things, and they come to confuse bigness with greatness. A glance at the New York skyline or PLAYBOY's pinup centerfold amply demonstrates what I'm talking about. This is not to say something can't be big *and* great. But just because something *is* big (or numerous or long-lasting), that doesn't mean the quality is there. That old saw about "It ain't what you got, it's what you do with it" rings true.

When I say plus ten, I don't want to imply that that's an absolute number.

Plus ten for me is total aliveness.

That's not a measure—that's a direction.

CHAPTER

5

Readiness,
Purposefullness,
and Hopefullness

I'm an unashamed fan of what used to be called "three-hankie" movies, or "tearjerkers"—films that were in some way so stirring emotionally as to make it impossible to dam the tears. Oh, the flood of pictures I am getting as I write this! I see the handless veteran Harold Russell (in *The Best Years of Our Lives,* his only film) embracing his prewar girl friend for the first time, letting her see his hooks. In a movie about World War One, *Paths of Glory,* I see a German girl pushed in front of French soldiers and told to sing; as her frail but clear voice fills the huge room, the hooting and jeering soldiers calm, then begin to get tears in their eyes as they join her in singing "Lili Marlene." I think of children trudging across China with Ingrid Bergman in *The Inn of the Sixth Happiness,* singing "This Old Man." I see a doctor, played by Lew Ayres of course, introducing the deaf-mute Jane Wyman to music in *Johnny*

Belinda by placing her hand on a violin that is being played by a friend; as she feels the vibrations, her face changes from curiosity to excitement. And I weep.

The perfect example of this type of movie is *Enchanted Cottage*. Herbert Marshall is a blind pianist and Robert Young is a pilot whose face was horribly scarred by flames and Dorothy McGuire is a homely whatever, and they come to this enchanted cottage, where Herbert Marshall can't even see what they look like. All he can sense is the growing love that happens between these two people, and at some point in the movie the pilot's burned face disappears and Dorothy McGuire's homeliness disappears because they're in love.

Yeahhhhh. It's movies like that that I love because they're all about the will to believe. To believe in the reality of fantasy. To believe in the "could be" on the screen. To be moved, emotionally, by the moving pictures. To be ready!

It's just being open, ready to meet something or someone or some idea that is new. It's being available to that which so many of us apparently dread—change. It's Maslow's stepping into the future unfettered, unfearful. It's the poet John Keats writing that "The only means of strengthening one's intellect is to make up one's mind about nothing—to let the mind be a thoroughfare for all thoughts."

GETTING OFF THE DIME: SOME DO, SOME DON'T

Sometimes the "dime" you are supposed to get off seems as large as a parade ground that is overgrown with thorny bushes to inhibit or block the traveler's way. "I can never do that . . . I can't change . . . it's too hard . . . it'll take too long": The Greek chorus wails on and on.

Almost everyone with a sexual problem goes through a period of putting things off. Andy hadn't slept with Patti in nearly three years, although they continued to live together. I asked them what they had done about the problem so far. She said she'd urged him to talk to someone, at least a friend. He always said he would but never did. Andy told me, "I'm probably the biggest procrastinator in the world."

Many others go through a period of lethargy or inactivity. Every therapist in the world has heard this line from hundreds of people with every kind of problem imaginable: "During all the time that I've had this problem, the way I would handle it was to try to ignore it and hope that somehow, magically, it would go away."

Whereas others seem completely directionless. With this sort I keep picturing a couple coming into a strange town and asking a good Samaritan to assist them because they're lost. And the good Samaritan says, "Of course, where would you like to go?" And the couple says, "We don't know."

Still others merely say that change is too difficult, requires too much work. "How," they ask, "can I unlearn thirty years of bad habits . . . it'll take me forever." Unfortunately, many therapists reinforce this point of view by sharing it. "How indeed," they say, "with a mother like yours, and a relationship like the one you had with your first husband? I should like to begin seeing you three times weekly, and at the end of six months or a year . . ." My God. If I heard that, I'd be intimidated, too.

Obviously these people were not in a state of readiness. Yet.

Others were very much ready.

The Viscount Montgomery, the leader of Britain's North African army during World War Two, said, "I am not a bit anxious about my battles. If I am anxious I don't fight them. I wait until I am ready." This is a philosophy, or point of view, that may easily be transferred to more peaceful aims, to the movement not of armies but individuals.

I remember Richard, the fiftyish businessman from Palo Alto, and his wife, Marie, who had been married for 25 years. Richard didn't know it, but he was already in a great state of readiness when he arrived in my office.

"For some twenty-two of those twenty-five years," he said, "I was of the opinion that our sex life was to all intents and purposes normal. Then three years ago the business started to allow some more time to one's self, and I realized that time was passing. I was nearing fifty and I started to look at the way our life-style was, sexually. And I found that my wife, while she accommodated my wishes sexually, never initiated sexual approaches. And because we have an excellent communication, discussions revealed, in her own words, that she just wasn't turned on."

Richard wanted to know what to do. How, he wondered, could he pump sexual life back into a relationship marked by "sameness" and which was, quite literally, an interlude during television commercials. He confided that he had been dining with a woman he met at work, usually with several of her friends, but recently he found himself alone with her. It was then that he experienced readiness, although, as I say, he didn't recognize the state at that time.

"As it turned out," he said, "the situation that particular evening was resolved for me. Instead of returning to the lady's apartment, which was my intention as well as hers, I met friends who precluded such an action and we broke up. However, it did awaken the feeling within me that if I felt this way toward another woman, there should be some ways of initiating those feelings within me for my wife. What I'm saying is that you're listening to a fellow who wants to find the way, to make it with his wife, who wants to maintain his marriage, who doesn't want to look around outside his marriage for sexual satisfaction, and who has the willingness to learn new styles and be taught new techniques or whatever."

Richard was experiencing readiness. He had accepted the possibility of a Right (Artistic) Brain, and once he had recognized its possible existence, he was free to imagine what he might do with it. Can *you* imagine using what's there, even if you're not sure what it is? Can you imagine doing that right now? Even if you're not certain what "doing that" means? Can you admit the possibility that you might have the answers in a brain you didn't know you had? Does that sound so far out, really?

The best part is, it's easy. Thomas Jefferson said, "Nothing is troublesome that we do willingly."

To be willing is to be ready.

BUILDING RESPONSE-ABILITY

What we're talking about here is responsibility, which is one of the major areas of exploration in the humanistic movement. The question is: Who owns the problem? The answer is: I do.

If people only knew that they're in charge of their emotions, that they're cause rather than effect.

"Oh, that s.o.b. got me angry!" someone cries.

No, no, no, that person did whatever it was that he or she did and, yes, he may be a son of a bitch, but *you* got angry. If you can't reach orgasm, it will serve no one for you to lie there helplessly, waiting for Mr. Right to come along. If you experience pain during intercourse, you can do something to relieve or eliminate that discomfort. If you're bored in bed, it's only because you're bored in bed, not because someone is boring you.

Buffy's problem was she thought that sex was dirty, *really* dirty. She said, "I feel if I have to satisfy my sexual desires, I would rather masturbate and hide in a closet by myself and not let anyone see me or know, rather than to get into bed and have sexual pleasures with my husband. I dislike seeing my husband's body naked. I dislike it very much. I don't like touching his genital area at all. It really bothers me. I get lumps in my throat, I feel very uncomfortable. I feel pressure and I'm very tense inside. When we have foreplay beforehand, I just don't get aroused. I'm wondering in my subconscious mind if the neighbors are hearing me, if the kids are going to wake up. When we do have sex, I have a problem of getting off him or getting him off me and going to clean myself up."

My response to all this (and there was more, lots more) was, "That's very interesting, Buffy, but tell me, how much longer do you intend to think sex is yuccchy?"

Chuck was really down when he came in. "Failure has been a major portion of my life," he said. "No matter what I do, I feel as if I'm failing. I really like my work, but my supervisor makes me feel my moves are wrong. I've never had any friends, really. I've never been able to command a situation. I always feel I am saying or doing the wrong thing at the wrong time. I feel schizo, as if there's another person within me who doesn't want me to have sex. Everything is falling apart. My car, work, people around me, the girl I was going with is not going out with me, she's going with someone else. She wants sex and I can't do anything about it. Premature ejaculation always occurs with me, even when I don't have an erect penis. Physical love has been a total lack in my life."

I listened to Chuck and I asked him, "How much longer do you wish to remain so unhappy?"

Natasha said, "I didn't take an active part in sex when I was in college. I just lay there until Tommy got satisfied.

Then we got married, and pretty soon we tapered off to maybe once or twice a month. This was followed by a forced sex situation, where I went off the pill to get pregnant, and that took almost a year. It was terrible. We were forcing ourselves to do something our heart really wasn't into doing. I don't think either one of us was satisfied emotionally. I got uptight about sex. I wasn't getting pregnant and I felt it was something I had to do to *get* pregnant. Then when I did get pregnant, I found I lost most of my interest in sex. After having so little sex and then so much, now our sex life just about came to a close. I guess it started when I got so trained in my head as a teen-ager to hold back and not fully enjoy what was going on with me sexually, because I might get pregnant or someone might find out or whatever. And then when I got married and it was okay to do that, I was in such a habit of thinking of not fully enjoying myself that maybe I couldn't let go."

I looked at Natasha and asked, "When do you intend to let go? How much longer do you care to hang on to the past?"

This question usually confuses my clients. They look startled, then puzzled. "What?" they ask, blankly.

"I said, 'How much longer do you intend to be the way you are, hanging on to the past?' ('How much longer do you intend to think sex is yucchy . . . wish to remain so unhappy, etc.?') 'For a week? Will you feel the same way *next* Tuesday?' "

My clients usually are smiling by now. They think I am being silly and often say so. They think I am joking. A very few are embarrassed. A few others are still confused.

I say, "Look at it this way. I believe that hardly anyone lets pain be transitory. Some people hang on to it tenaciously, as if their continued life on the planet depended on its presence. I think it's possible *not* to extend the depression any more of a courtesy than what is normally extended to having an orgasm . . ."

At this point, my client may think, "Having an orgasm? What's that got to do with it?" Or: "Having an orgasm? I *can't* have an orgasm . . . that's why I'm here!"

I coax the client into the game. "It's a stupid game, but . . . can you tell me how long an orgasm lasts? In minutes, or seconds? What do you think?"

Most will guess around ten seconds for the male and about two or three times that for women. Masters and Johnson say the duration varies—more widely for women than for men—but always it can be counted in seconds.

"That's not very long for a peak experience," I say. "Look, let's try something. If we say that an orgasm lasts ten seconds, let's extend that same time limit to the depression. For right now. Can you try it? Close your eyes and when I say, 'Go,' really get into your depression, and when I say, 'Stop,' get out of it. Ready?"

I check my watch and say, "Go." Ten seconds later I say, "Stop," and tell the client to open his or her eyes. Then I ask, "How do you feel?"

Nine times out of ten the answer is, "Still depressed."

"Right," I say. "Now we're going to do it again, but this time when I say 'Stop,' remember the best orgasm you ever had. Remember what it was like when you experienced it. Remember exactly where it felt so good, and who you were with and what you said, and how hot you felt. Really get into that orgasm. And hold the feeling for ten seconds. First the depression, then the orgasm. Ready? Go . . ."

I ask clients who have never experienced orgasm to get a picture of whatever it was that turned them on most. Maybe it's a hole in one on the golf course, or listening to a church choir singing Handel's *Messiah*, or eating chocolate cream pie, or kissing the one they love. I tell them to get a clear picture of a peak experience . . . and hold it for ten seconds.

I ask my clients to play this game with themselves whenever they catch themselves in a depression over a sex problem. It's like doing what mothers and fathers do for their young children when they fall down; they kiss them where it hurts. Giving yourself an orgasm in fantasy when you are depressed is like kissing yourself where it hurts.

Best of all, it is taking charge. You see, I just can't pat someone on the back and say, "That's okay, it'll be all right." Because I don't believe it *will* be all right unless you know it *can* be and then *do* something about it. Poets always know the truth about such things. William Blake wrote, "He who desires but acts not, breeds pestilence."

This was psychiatrist Bill Glasser's point of view in *Reality Therapy*. What, he asked, do you intend to do? His definition of responsibility is a good one. He says it's "the ability to fulfill one's needs, and to do so in a way that does not deprive others of the ability to fulfill their needs."

I like that. What Glasser is saying is really little different from the so-called hippie ethic of the 1960s: Do your thing, but don't lay your trip on someone else. What's important to notice is that from all these sources the focus is on *doing*. Changing. Expanding. Shifting. Reframing. Becoming.

Becoming more responsible is figuring out what our purpose is. See, some people have a purpose in having a problem. They believe it's *so good* to have a problem to work on. It is as if they are saying, "It would all be so meaningless without this problem. If I didn't have this problem, what would I have?"

Other people are afraid to let go because they figure their present problem will be replaced by another. So they hang on to their problems rather apathetically, say-

ing, "Well, at least I know *this* problem, I've learned how
to live with it, sort of. I don't want to stir everything up
again." Come weal or come woe, the status is quo.

For others, purpose is something greater than that.
Norbert Wiener wrote in *The Human Use of Human
Beings*, "There is one quality more important than 'know-
how' and we cannot accuse the United States of any
undue amount of it. This is 'know-what,' by which we
determine not only how we accomplish our purposes, but
what our purposes are to be."

Now we're talking about setting goals. We have become
responsible . . . response-able, *able* to respond and *ready*
to respond. Now we decide the ways in which we choose
to respond.

SETTING GOALS

I was always wishing as a kid . . . wishing for this and
wishing for that. And I was always pretty careful not to
wish for things that were impossible. I mean, I didn't want
to fail. I remember wishing I had good grades in high
school, so I could go on to college, and I remember wishing
I had good grades in college so I could go on to medical
school. And I noticed that I had a lot to do with making
those wishes real.

It was goal clarification. I asked myself: What did I
want? And: What was I willing to do for what I wanted?
And I was always willing to work for what I wanted.
Always. And I guess I can demand no less from anyone
I see in my practice.

So what I'm asking for now, besides readiness and high
intention, is a willingness to pursue, while cautioning you
not to program yourself for failure.

By don't program yourself for failure, I mean don't set
your sights too high, initially, or give yourself an unrea-

sonable deadline . . . for example, "Tonight I come, or else!" William Penn, the Quaker who founded Philadelphia, put it this way: "Never give out while there is hope; but hope not beyond reason, for that shows more desire than judgment."

By don't program yourself for failure, I mean don't let your liabilities get in the way of your assets. For example, Doris notices that she only has orgasms with men she truly loves (that's an asset), but she continues to bounce from man to man, most of them married (that's a liability).

I always ask my clients what it is they want . . . what is it that they would like their sexual relationship to be? What is their specific goal? Most demonstrate both readiness and a clear sense of purpose. Here are several typical responses:

> I think I want to develop in myself an awareness for my partner again, a feeling of how to know, understand, and help him to solve his and our problem. I think it's his problem on his own, but then putting us together it's our problem. I want him to be able to solve his problem and I think I can help him do it. Should our relationship go that we wind up breaking up and going our separate ways, I'd like to know he no longer has his problem.

> My goals are the hopes that my wife and I can achieve an ability to have good, pleasurable, reasonably uninhibited, frequent sexual relations with each other with mutual physical and emotional pleasure from them. I would like to have my wife's inhibitions about sexual response greatly reduced and her ability to be aroused and find sexual fulfillment developed to a much greater degree. I would be happy for myself if I could also be able to be a little more relaxed in our sexual relationship and perhaps

be able to talk more freely with my wife during the times when we are making love.

What I would like is to be able to fully experience and enjoy sex, including orgasms. I feel I've put up some kind of emotional barrier and I want to do whatever is necessary to break down that barrier.

I would like to relieve the fears and awkwardness and anxiety that I feel in contemplating any physical or sexual experience with my wife. I'd like to see that we find ourselves so attracted to one another that nothing stands in the way of our pleasant physical experience. It doesn't even have to be intercourse. It can be love play, or petting, or what have you, all of which I now find usually threatening and awkward.

I want to learn how to fall in love with him all over again.

I just want one very simple little thing . . . I want to just all of a sudden, just really, really love sex . . . just crave it . . . and not be able to get enough of it. I know it can be really, really neat and I want to get that excited feeling that I used to have before I was married.

What I want is to feel like I'm supervirile and a man who loves his wife enough to care about her sexually. I want to feel that when I come home it's like coming home to a turned-on woman, someone who can turn me on. And I want her to have the superest orgasm she could ever have, because I think that would really turn me on and fulfill the magic dream that I have . . . that one day I'll actually turn her on.

I want to have sexual intercourse with my husband in our home in our bed every night and every morning from now on. I can't think of anything nicer.

All these goals are reasonable, and they are generous. It is clear that the individuals and couples seeking assistance are ready to give and care and love. These are terrific goals. They are the goals of people preparing to leap from the zero-to-minus-ten side of their sexuality into the zero-to-plus-ten side. These are sexual "losers" on the brink of becoming sexual "winners."

THE FINAL MAGICAL INGREDIENT: HOPEFULLNESS

There's little I like to do more than to browse in my big Oxford Dictionary or rummage through collections of quotations. You won't even find "hope*full*ness," because it really isn't a word. But you will find a lot has been said about hope. And that's what "hope*full*ness" is all about . . . it is to be full up to here with hope.

Many of the quotations are negative, cynical—from Alexander Pope, who wrote that "Hope springs eternal in the human breast:/Man never is, but always to be blest," to Don Marquis, who had his typewriting cockroach archie say, "the only way boss/to keep hope in the world/is to keep changing its/population frequently."

Of course I disagree. However much I have enjoyed both these writers, I believe they are wrong about hope. Man *is* blessed, and one of the things he is blessed with is hope. It is only when he relies on hope alone that the blessing comes to pieces. To be full of hope but without purpose or readiness defines another, opposite state, what I call *hope emptiness*. Some people call that *hopelessness*, but I can't believe that *hopeless* is the opposite of *hopefull*; *hopeless*, to me, is the opposite of *hopemore*.

I assume this isn't confusing. It's just that when people tell me their position is hopeless, I tend to think that means they are not without hope (hope empty), but merely somewhat less than hope*full*. On a scale it would look like this:

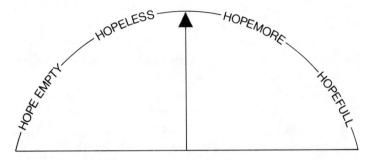

When people understand this, I can say, "When you're convinced your situation is hopeless, remember that it could be worse." And, of course, "Remember that it could be more or full."

Let's aim for hope*full*ness, the state of being full of hope. Aristotle called hope "a waking dream," and the French novelist Georges Bernanos said it was "a risk that must be run." The Oxford Dictionary says it is "desire plus expectation." They are all good definitions.

Desire is wishing, craving, longing for something pleasurable. (Also the first stage of the DAO—desire, arousal, orgasm—cycle.) Add expectation, and you add favorable anticipation, the condition of being likely, that which is expected, probability. It is to wish and to know that it *could* (or may) come true.

For example, faith healing is a little-understood phenomenon that seems to be related to the influence the emotions have on the body. A person's feelings can bring about dramatic changes in his or her physiological functioning. Many believe that in some cases of faith healing—where people throw away their crutches and walk, for instance—it is the sick person's strong "faith" in the power of the healer that may actually bring about the desired physical changes. The healer knows he hasn't any such power. He is but a facilitator who knows the people have the power within themselves.

Oral Roberts is a modern faith healer who tells people to "Expect a Miracle." He is not surprised when the miracles arrive. Norman Vincent Peale was talking about the same phenomenon when he made the title of his best-selling book, *The Power of Positive Thinking*, a part of the language. So, too, are so many in the human potential movement who speak of "affirmations," rewarding yourself repeatedly during each day with statements like "I deserve a new and exciting job . . . I am worthy of praise . . . I am moving toward a healthy, sharing sex life . . ."

Why not tell yourself how good you are? After all, what is the alternative? *The Little Engine That Could* surely would have had a more satisfying, and possibly quicker, journey uphill in that children's story if he had said not "I think I can, I think I can, I think I can . . ." but "I know I can, I know I can, I know I can . . ."

Set it up. Make it easy. Give yourself a break.

A final quotation about hope, from John F. Kennedy, several years before he was elected to the presidency: "We should not let our fears hold us back from pursuing our hopes."

6

Learning Sex Can Be Fun

David learned many things during his adolescent years. He learned how to put the shot. He learned a little French, including all the words to one smutty French song. He learned how to dance with girls. With a few of his friends on the playground one day he even learned how to chew and spit tobacco, although afterward he said he had no desire to try it again.

During the same period, and in the years that followed, he also learned what he later described as "premature ejaculation." Of course I don't like that label, but it is clear that whatever the problem is called, David could reach the orgasmic state in almost no time at all. And it is just as clear that this was learned behavior.

How did David learn to come so fast? It was easy. First he engaged in hurried masturbation in the bathroom to avoid being caught by his parents or his meddlesome younger brother. Later came a few masturbatory contests with the same friends he chewed tobacco with, only now the object wasn't to expectorate/ejaculate the farthest but the fastest. There were several instances of petting to a climax without intercourse, in the local lovers' lanes, where he finally did begin to have intercourse, and remained in a hurry, for fear of being caught. When he and some of the guys visited prostitutes, the session was kept quick and methodical; by now, David didn't even notice that the girl was in a hurry (to take care of another customer). More than that, I don't think David—and this is typical—ever wanted to give a girl a chance to change her mind. He wanted to get it over with fast before she had second thoughts about what she was doing.

In this way David, and many other men, have *learned* to have an orgasm problem. The process (mode) by which he learned this is called *classical conditioning,* or learning by association. This is the field of psychology founded by the Russian physiologist Ivan Pavlov, who taught dogs to associate meat powder with the ringing of a tuning fork and a bell; after a while, the association was so firmly set that the dogs began to salivate to the tuning fork alone.

In the years since Pavlov's first experiments, classical conditioning has been studied in human behavior and today is generally thought to be one of the most important ways we learn. For example, when a child sees mother put on her apron, an action usually identified with her preparing dinner, the child, like the puppy, may also begin to salivate. Similarly, a driver learns to respond to a red light by stopping his car, and a man or a woman learns to have stronger sexual responses to one individual than to another.

And so David learned to associate sexual intercourse— or sex of any sort, for that matter—with rapid ejaculation; they were as positively linked as mama's apron and dinner, as closely as red and stop.

Many other common sexual complaints are learned in much the same way. Eva, for example, said she could not experience orgasm through intercourse. "There's been persistent pain connected with sex for many years," she said. "When I was about nineteen, during one of my first sexual relationships, I developed a Bartholin's gland cyst and it had to be operated on, and it recurred three times and each time it had to be operated on. Ever since then, at various times, very frequently, it's bothered me again during intercourse. Also, about six years ago I developed a bladder infection and it was treated, but the pain recurs occasionally, especially after intercourse. So I've come to associate intercourse with pain in a way."

So many women come in with the same problem, complaining of an inability to reach a climax with intercourse, fearing sex with their partners because of the pain generally associated with it. Within minutes, these women are revealing how they *learned* to be that way.

My first sexual experience of intercourse was with my husband. I remember it being very painful.

I've built up such a mental block about having constant yeast infections all the time, every time he'd touch me there, it would just ache and hurt.

In the very early years of our marriage I found sex physically and emotionally not only distasteful, but also very, very unpleasant and almost abhorrent. I hated it. Physically it was uncomfortable. I'm sure now that was because I had no or little secretion, so all I got was a lot of friction and irritation and soreness.

Still other nonorgasmic women rooted their complaint in other fears. Remember Natasha, who always "shut down" when sexual intercourse started, because when she was a teen-ager she worried about getting pregnant or discovered? Although now married, she said, "I feel all those years of shutting down just kind of became ingrained." Whereas Doris believed that she wasn't experiencing orgasms because of her "fear of failure." "At first it wasn't all that important," she said, "because I'd missed a few times with my old man. But after we broke up, although I went to bed with a lot of men, I felt nothing. Now, after a year of failure with many people, I'm disgusted at even being touched."

These women were experiencing pain or panic or some other negative emotion by association. Some experienced the "shutdown" or pain at the first sign of sexual contact, before intercourse was attempted. Just like Pavlov's dog.

PAYING THE SEXUAL CONSEQUENCES

Another common mode or process of learning is called *operant conditioning*. This is learning from the consequences, learning on the basis of reward and punishment, which in psychology are called *positive* and *negative reinforcement*. It is this process that is generally used to train animals; to get fed, a dolphin must jump through a burning hoop and a chicken must play the piano. This is the territory so carefully studied and mapped by Harvard psychologist B. F. Skinner, who taught pigeons to do amazing things, including playing Ping Pong.

Similarly among humans, a toddler will learn to control his bowels for applause from his parents; a child will learn to turn a key in a door in order to be rewarded with entrance into the house. Thus people learn to step on the brake pedal in order to stop the automobile, and to smile at someone from whom they want a smile back.

Now, some psychologists say this Skinnerian stuff sometimes sounds awfully Pavlovian. There's a controversy about this. I don't care. It is enough for me to notice (whether it is by "association" or because of the "consequences") that the behavior is *learned*.

The very first time a couple engages in sexual intercourse a variety of judgments may be rendered by either party. Let's imagine that discomfort and disappointment were to occur. Such an outcome (punishment) would likely be perceived as upsetting since pleasure was anticipated. Neither person may wish to communicate his or her displeasure, believing that this could only aggravate further an already unpleasant condition. Were it to recur the next time, it would be easy to understand how one or both partners might reach the conclusion that sex isn't fun.

Remember Buffy, who thought sex was dirty, really dirty? Well, no wonder. She learned that it was dirty when she was young. As she was growing up, there were several instances when she was "punished" for engaging in such dirtiness. Listen to part of her touching story:

"I remember when I was a little girl, the first time I masturbated my mother caught me. That night I got the worst licking of my life from both of my parents, mostly from my mother. And really degrading me with words, saying what a bad girl I was for masturbating, telling me if I masturbated anymore I wasn't going to have children and people would think I was a bad girl. Then the next day she got me in the car and drove me to the doctor's office. I can vividly see his office. He sat me on top of his table and told me, 'Young lady, you're a very bad, naughty girl.'

"I remember when I started my period for the very first time, my older half-sister broadcast it all over the high school. 'Ha-ha, my young sister has become a young lady!' I was very embarrassed and felt just terrible. She told all of her friends, whom I highly respected.

"My first sexual experience of intercourse was with my husband-to-be. I remember it being very painful. It hurt.

I didn't enjoy it. I cried. And because of that I became pregnant. I was eighteen at the time, it was my birthday. He put his fraternity pin on my chest and, boom, that night we went to bed. He maneuvered himself very easily into me and, boy, did it hurt! And I felt very, very guilty about it.

"It hurt when we went home and I told my mother I was pregnant. She called me every name in the book, from a whore to a goddamn prostitute. She said I wasn't allowed to walk down the aisle in the church, or wear white. We went to see a priest and we told him of the circumstances. He told me I was a dirty whore and that people who did that were down in the red-light district. I had committed a mortal sin . . .

"I remember all during the pregnancy I wasn't allowed to visit my hometown. My mother said she would lose face and maybe lose her job as a teacher. I had it put on me that my mother had a nervous breakdown because of my pregnancy."

Is it any wonder that Buffy learned that sex was yuccchy?

MODELING IS MORE THAN A CAREER

To me, the most exciting way for people to learn is not Pavlovian and it's not Skinnerian. There's a man at Stanford University named Albert Bandura who's done a lot of work on *modeling*—vicarious learning, observational modeling. These terms or phrases cover any learning process where the person changes or picks up behavior as a result of observing, and copying, the behavior of another person . . . in person, on television, or from a book.

Examples of this learning process are common, for many of our most personal habits were openly copied from the grown-up idols who were around as we passed through the various development stages. Even as we took our first steps we were beginning to place our feet and swing our hips just as our primary models did. A little girl learns how to walk like mom and talk like mom and possibly even think like mom, at least about certain things. And if mom is a smoker, chances are daughter will grow up to be one. If mom or dad is a child-beater, probably the child will be a child-beater too.

Much sexual behavior is learned in the same way:

—Phyllis complained that she couldn't talk about sex with her partners, and later it came out that her parents avoided the subject and even went so far as to spell out the word s-e-x in conversation.

—Many men and women learn to masturbate by following instructions given by a friend, or observing that friend in the act of masturbating. And "circle jerks" produce "quick triggers."

—Tania remembers how much her mother complained about her sex life, always calling her father "a lousy lay and a lousy cheat besides." She told Tania all men were that way, and Tania believed her.

—Cherie's mom told her it hurt, and Cherie believed that.

—Ted's idol in high school was a sexually active football player, so he too became a "stud," ricocheting from conquest to conquest for years, never developing a meaningful relationship; he also modeled himself on his father, who drank and beat his mother up on Saturday nights.

—Ernie took his cue from his wife. She was non-orgasmic, so he developed an erection problem in sympathy. (It is also common for women to lose all sexual desire when their partners are experiencing erection failure.)

The world of popular entertainment has offered other dubious models in this area. In 1972, Linda Lovelace set a demanding new standard in fellatio, and thousands choked on it. Marlon Brando and Maria Schneider presented anal sex in *Last Tango in Paris*. David Bowie and Mick Jagger epitomized androgyny, representing a blurred sexual identity. The reigning sex idols were male chauvinists (Burt Reynolds, Clint Eastwood) and plasticized look-but-don't-touch teases (Raquel Welch, Farrah Fawcett-Majors, the Playmate of the Month). In the best-selling *Fear of Flying*, Erica Jong contributed the "zipless fuck" to the cause of sexual noncommitment.

So far I've only looked at the ways sexual losers learned how to be sexual losers. Now the good news: These same learning modes, or processes, may also be used to create sexual winners.

BREAKING BAD HABITS IS IMPOSSIBLE— WHAT TO DO INSTEAD

Attempts are often made at breaking or eliminating bad habits. Such efforts are frequently unsuccessful. Over 50 percent of smokers who try to quit go back to smoking as soon as a stressful situation comes up, even though they are aware that smoking is dangerous to health. The figures are no more encouraging among the sexually dissatisfied, who find themselves returning to their old behaviors even though they may have tried the best "unlearning" or "habit-breaking" techniques.

What is "unlearning"? Well, if to learn means to acquire or gain, then unlearn means to take away or lose. But it is questionable whether behavior is ever truly lost, even when it is no longer observable. For example, people who have stopped smoking still know how to smoke; if given a cigarette they would know precisely how to light it, inhale it, knock off the ash, and so on. Just as one-time bicycle riders who haven't been on a two-wheeler in years still know how to ride a bicycle. And long-ago roller skaters can still, however awkwardly, roller-skate.

Skills and bad habits can coexist along with the many other items of behavior a person has in his or her repertoire —even when the skills (assets) and bad habits (liabilities) seem incongruous and contradictory.

The human mind is fantastic. It has an incredible capacity to add on. Whatever you want to put in there you can put in there. Most people understand that. We are very powerful and we don't notice how powerful we are. Psychiatrists, unfortunately, are thought of as "shrinks." One of these days we'll all realize that if we want to go for assistance we'll go to an "expand." Really. Not to a "shrink." For one thing, it's not true –you can't take away anything from a person's past. No matter what you do, it will always be there, a part of that person's history. Besides, why bother?

They're playing with habit-breaking—psychologists call it "extinguishing behavior"—in some of our public schools. It's idiocy . . . from my point of view. The truth is, bad habits are best noticed and left alone. I believe it's much better to have people decide for themselves what they want to learn and then have them learn. A person desirous of changing behavior need only acquire new behavior and then select it for use when appropriate.

For example, an English-speaking person who wants to converse in Portuguese need only acquire an ability to speak Portuguese and then use this new language (behavior) by choice. Nothing need be done to the English-speaking behavior already present, right? What is important to notice is that if the person *chooses*, he may never speak English again (while retaining the ability, should he or she ever wish to), and thereafter speak only Portuguese.

SEX IS NOT PORTUGUESE—WHAT IS IT?

Of course, learning about sexual satisfaction is not exactly like learning how to speak Portuguese. Berlitz guarantees you will be speaking fluent Portuguese in a specific amount of time. Sexual happiness never comes prepackaged and guaranteed that way. But the same principles apply. A person wishing to change sexual behavior may leave that behavior alone and instead acquire new behavior, then select it for use by choice.

People who do this are the sexual winners, and their stories are told in the following 12 chapters.

7

How to Tell Your Assets from Your Elbow

Two chapters ago I considered Readiness, Purposefullness, and Hopefullness. That was a chapter about Desire, or Motivation, the first phase in the sexual (life) cycle.

In the last chapter I considered the learning process. This represented Arousal, or Participation, the second phase in the cycle.

This chapter, about recognizing and using assets well, is the first of 12 devoted to Orgasm, or Intense Excitement . . . and that completes the cycle.

Once upon a time in a modern nursery in a modern hospital in a modern city a newborn boy got an old-fashioned erection.

That's when the trouble started.

The nurse bathing the little boy smiled knowingly. Another nurse noticed the erection and said, "Who's the stud, Mary?"

Mary laughed. "These men!" she said. "They're *born* horny."

Neither nurse noticed that the boy's twin sister in the next crib was also aroused. In females sexual arousal is usually indicated by vaginal wetness. Nurses and doctors . . . and parents, for that matter . . . don't notice when such wetness occurs in female infants, usually because they don't look. And if they did, they'd probably just shrug and say, "She's wet . . . what infant isn't?"

Which of the following "rules" apply to this scene?

1. Bigger (breasts/penis/etc.) is better.
2. Sex is dirty; only do it with someone you love. (That's a rule grown-ups have for teen-agers.)
3. Good girls don't do it. (Another parent/teen rule.)
4. Grandparents don't do it either.
5. Males are always ready.
6. Females have to "be made" ready.
7. Self-stimulation is not okay when you're with some-one else.
8. Males need erections to make love.
9. Sex must be spontaneous and/or natural.
10. No one talks about it in polite company.
11. Pornography breeds perverts.
12. Couples that come together stay together.

This list goes on endlessly, chronicling the popular mythology of our sexually confused and frustrated times. These are "rules" which have been passed down through the ages, from generation to generation, with consummate love and blind prejudice. In the past few years many of these rules, or myths, have been challenged. And there are many people who have abandoned these rules. But there are millions who haven't. Yet.

The notion is that little children learn early that they don't do anything right. They don't eat properly. They don't sleep all through the night. They defecate in their pants. They don't know how to walk, or talk, or dress themselves. Later they learn that they don't know how to work ovens and cars and all the things that surround them. They don't know *anything*. That's what we tell them. And they learn it fast. Some carry this feeling of inferiority or inadequacy throughout life.

Mightn't it be different if we merely taught children that they didn't know how to eat and walk and talk and be courteous *yet*? Mightn't it be different if rules like these didn't exist? If desire, arousal, and orgasm could just be that, if life's cycle of motivation, participation, and intense excitement could just be that, and we didn't notice; you see, evaluation and judgment are based on "rules" which say we're not perfect. Rules say someone else is "better," or "bigger," or "lasts longer," or "comes more times."

Rules!

13. It's better in the dark.
14. Coitus counts . . . that's the right (normal) way.
15. The man always makes the first move.
16. Teen-age pregnancy is a problem.
17. Married people don't masturbate.
18. Nobody nice, married or otherwise, masturbates.

I had a call in Seattle once from an institution, and they knew I was interested in sex. The gentleman on the telephone said, "Would you come and help us teach our 'unteachables'?"

I said, "Well, I don't know about your 'unteachables.' What do you want to teach them?"

"Well, about sex."

I said, "Depends what you want to teach them about sex. A lot of them probably know already."

He said, "That's what I mean. We want you to come and teach them. We don't like what they do. We catch them. We catch them doing things they ought not to do."

I thought this would be interesting, so I went and I found out how people catch people. It's fascinating how you catch people. If you want to figure out how to catch people, you can. There seem to be many institutions, in government as well as in mental health, where people are very adept at that. I talked with the kids, and after I saw what they did, I said, "I didn't notice that any of your kids defecated in the living room."

And the person drew himself up and said, "*Our* children don't *defecate* in the living room."

I said, "Well, then they're teachable. They don't pee on the carpets. They're all regimented, they all do things. Of course they're teachable. All people are teachable. Everybody learns. Some just learn faster, or slower, than others and so what. You want me to teach them that touching themselves is bad, evil, sinful? Teach them that they'll go to hell? You can teach them that. You're doing that right now. Ask them if they've learned. Some of them have, but they touch themselves anyhow. They probably figure it's worth the chance. Hell's far away."

You know, parents (and other authority figures) are remarkable. Little kids touch their nose, and their proud parents coo, "Johnny touch nose." But if a little kid touches his genitals, the reaction is, "*Stop that!*" Some people think that if a kid touches his genitals it's masturbating. It's not. It's touching his genitals. There's really a big difference between masturbating and touching your genitals. Some people haven't recognized that. Yet.

Rules!

19. All marital relationships are salvageable.
20. All sexual problems are resolvable.
21. Male on top.

22. Women aren't turned on by pornography.
23. My way is the wrong way.

Rules are not writ in blazing letters across the evening sky. The truth is, they're only points of view . . . somebody's opinion. Who says bigger is better? Who says males are always ready and females have to be primed? (The rules coming out of the hospital nursery scene.) Who says you have to masturbate alone? Who says males need erections to be terrific lovers? Who says?

As we come of age we pile up a listing of rules that would not slip by in even the most repressive state legislature, yet many people believe in these rules (laws) and live by them as if a long jail sentence were the alternative. Can you imagine your state legislature passing a law that insisted bigger was better, or that females had to be "made ready," or that masturbation with your partner present was illegal?

Rules like these get people in trouble every day, make them miserable, shove them into the zero-to-minus-ten side of life's rating game. For example, Tim and Elizabeth were like a lot of people who were admonished not to screw when they were teenagers. Now they think that's all there is. Because if you're not supposed to do that, that's what you get to do when you decide not to listen to the people who say, "Don't do that." These people may never learn about anything else merely because they were taught that heterosexual intercourse was *it* . . . the beginning, the middle, and the end of sex. Which is okay if it serves them well. If they're exhilarated and fulfilled, terrific. But what happens when Elizabeth's depression following a hysterectomy causes her to "freeze up" every time Tim approaches her sexually? What happens when Tim gets a urological disease that leaves him impotent? The rule—intercourse is *it*, everything else is kinky—has left Tim and Elizabeth with nothing sexual to do.

Bjorn and Jenny had a similar problem. Bjorn was sent to me by an internist who worked in a diabetes clinic on one of our famous military installations. The guy hadn't been able to get it up for many years. After a couple of minutes of talk, I knew he'd never get it up, except with a surgical procedure, a sort of erector set that promises hydraulic erection, but doesn't promise ejaculation. Bjorn wasn't dating Jenny the way he used to. He wouldn't do certain things that he used to. Because he couldn't perform. And Jenny thought there was something wrong with *her*. So we talked about the many ways he used to turn her on and I asked if he needed an erection to turn her on. He thought about that seriously and said, "Probably not." He remembered times when he was tired and wasn't performing and she still had orgasms. I said, "How come you're not doing that anymore?" The last thing I heard was he was a better lover than he'd ever been. And I don't know that Jenny wasn't telling him that to make him feel better. But he was involved, fully participating, and getting intense excitement in a different variety of forms.

Who says an erection is mandatory? Who says? Rules! The truth is:

Whatever Works, Works

Achmed, a minister in the Vizier's cabinet in charge of official dogma and ritual, had heard reports that there were three peasants living across the lake who were developing a reputation among the villagers for being great sages. Knowing that there was no recognized teacher in that particular village, Achmed decided to investigate. So he boarded a boat and rowed across the lake.

Once on the other side, Achmed found the three men in question, sitting happily under a date palm.

"I hear you three are great sages," he said to them. "Do you know any of the recognized rituals?"

"We are but poor and uneducated peasants," said the first man. "We know nothing of sages or rituals," said the second. "We cannot even read," said the third, all of them beaming like the sun.

"Do you know any of the authorized prayers?" Achmed asked.

The three men admitted sadly that they did not. "We pray, but in our own simple way."

"Let me hear your prayer," the minister commanded. The three men closed their eyes and chanted in unison, "Oh Lord, may all share our joy."

"Aha!" said Achmed. "Just as I thought. That is not an authorized prayer."

The three men apologized profusely. "Oh, please teach us the proper manner of the rituals," they pleaded.

The minister consented to teach them the authorized liturgy. He recited a long chant, bowing precisely with all the correct gestures and subtle inflections. "We are too uneducated and illiterate to learn such an involved ritual," the three peasants proclaimed.

"I will teach you if it takes all night," Achmed said.

It did. The next morning, a very tired minister got into the boat and started rowing slowly back across the lake.

Halfway across, he heard his name being shouted. He turned to see the three men running across the water toward him, shouting, "Minister, please wait, we have forgotten one of the words in the ritual!"

Achmed bowed humbly to them as they approached the boat, saying, "Keep doing what you have always done. It is working."

This story is not new to anyone who has taken the *est* training or read Adam Smith's popular survey of the human potential movement, *Powers of Mind*. Coming originally from mystical Sufi writings, it shows clearly one of the means by which the Sufis believe man can better himself, develop new faculties (the Sufis include telepathy and prophecy in the game plan), and therefore move toward limitless perfectibility.

The Sufis tell us to *do what works*. That is so simple it is brilliant. Why do what *doesn't* work? Yet I know a lot of people who do that every day, or try to. I know nonorgasmic women who keep right on being nonorgasmic. I know men who call themselves "premature ejaculators" who keep ejaculating sooner than they think they should, night after night after night. I know men with erection problems, women with pain, couples up to here with boredom, all of whom keep right on doing all the same old things . . . the things that do not work. Isn't that odd?

Some people tell me nothing's working, and from nothing, as Shakespeare said, comes nothing. I suggest that such people might be letting their liabilities get in the way of their assets. Once a specific goal has been targeted—vaginal orgasm, reliable erection, more affection, whatever it may be—I've found it's worthwhile exploring with the client those items of cognitive (thinking), affective (feeling), and motor (doing) behavior already present in the client's repertoire. Some of these items are liabilities, others are assets. For many people, the assets seem invisible.

It is crucial first to note the person's liabilities and incongruities . . . that thinking, feeling, and doing behavior that seems to get in the way of the specified goal, especially the behavior that seems recurrent. Once noted (as I've said before), it may be left alone and another behavior chosen. This may take the form of newly acquired, regularly practiced and mastered skills. It may also be old behavior that works. This is called an asset, behavior already in the client's repertoire that may assist in reaching the specific goal.

Assets are good things from the past and present that can assist you in moving into your future comfortably. Assets are the Rightsided behavior you already have, and it doesn't matter how Leftsided the overall picture may seem . . . the assets are there to be used.

It's not necessary to abandon your past to pursue a happy tomorrow. Only notice that it's there, then let it go *if it doesn't serve you well*. Although much of your past and present might be left alone profitably, there might also be something there worth holding on to, worth nurturing. For example, Scrooge, the "villain" of Charles Dickens's *A Christmas Carol*, found redemption in remembering himself as a child, reading *The Arabian Nights*, possessed of an imagination after all. In the same way, when I stopped smoking I built upon all the nonsmoking behavior of my precollege years when I didn't smoke.

Meredith came to me with a common complaint . . . she wasn't experiencing orgasm in intercourse with her husband. The only time she did find satisfaction was alone, while wearing underpants and lying on her stomach with her thighs tightly crossed and her hands pressed firmly on her upper pubic area. She told me this was a masturbatory practice that she had begun at age seven or eight and had continued to the present. She didn't realize that this was an asset, that she already had behavior in her repertoire that worked, behavior she could expand and exploit to bring zero to plus-ten sex. She thought it too strange to admit to her husband. Besides that, she believed people masturbated alone.

She was told that not everyone did that alone; she was told that many people did it in front of each other and to each other, and enjoyed it. It was suggested she try that, then maybe further take advantage of what obviously worked and continue her masturbatory behavior, but with her husband, cutting a hole in the underpants to allow him to enter her from behind.

The example may seem unusual—Meredith herself called it "bizarre"—but I don't think it is. (Everything is normal, right?) No more unusual than the problem of Melinda, who said boredom and frustration ended her marriage and now she couldn't come with a partner. In recounting her sexual history, she said, "The first time I can remember having an orgasm was when I was about nineteen years old and I went to the beach with a boy and we engaged in necking and petting and it was just through physical contact I had an orgasm. I can remember it distinctly. And then a year later, after I graduated, again I went out with a boy and I had gone out with him many times. I liked him. I remember we had gone to the beach again, and coming home he put his head on my lap and began what you might call oral sex on his part and again I had an orgasm." This one nostalgic paragraph was laden with assets, but Melinda was either ignoring them or didn't know that's what they were.

First of all, she knew how to climax—she'd done it before—and she remembered distinctly what it felt like. That meant that her current problem probably wasn't physiological (it rarely is). And her memory made it possible for her to recreate that feeling in fantasy. Still another asset was in circumstance—how and where she reached orgasm when she was 19 and 20 years old. It wasn't by intercourse, but on the first occasion friction alone and on the second oral manipulation. And both instances were connected with the beach.

It was suggested she take her partner to the beach. Pavlov would've been proud. It worked.

Loretta was worried about her husband's drinking, said it left him "impotent," and with no sexual intercourse she felt deprived and he felt like a failure; it was destroying their marriage of 20 essentially happy years. I noticed that he said he sometimes experienced an erection in the morning, when, as he put it, "my bladder's full; it goes away when I urinate." Of course that has nothing to do with the morning erection. The truth is, a full bladder never produced an erection in a bar when a man was delaying a trip to the toilet, and it never produced one during sleep or anywhere or anytime else.

The morning hard-on is the product of something called REM sleep, the kind of sleep that comes approximately every 90 minutes and is most conducive to dreams. It was suggested that Loretta might want to talk to her husband about his drinking problem and in the meantime she might keep an eye peeled for those morning erections and, the next time she saw one, gently and lovingly use it well. That worked too.

Curtis told me he was a "premature ejaculator." Whenever anybody says that to me I instantly get a picture of a stopwatch and a vagina, and the story Curtis told didn't do anything to alter the image. I asked him what he meant by "premature ejaculation." He said, "I put it in and almost right away I come, before Dorothy is even warmed up."

"Tell me," I said, "do you ever masturbate, or did you before you were with Dorothy?"

"Well, sure. Not so much now but . . ."

"Good. Now tell me this. Did you ever come too fast when you masturbated?"

Curtis laughed. "You see," I said, "it's just a point of

view. You only come too fast when you're with someone else. Tell me, does it feel good? When you come?"

Curtis smiled and said, "Of course it does, but it would be better if . . ."

"Ah yes. Look, Curtis, I knew a person once who said, 'If only I could last seventeen minutes,' and I said to the person, 'Don't you know what will be going on in your head, setting it up that way—just as you make seventeen a voice will say, 'Eighteen . . . eighteen. . . .' Curtis, what you've got now . . . dig it, it's great. It is, isn't it? You said it feels good, right?

"Well, go with it. You know how to come fast, so the next time you're with Dorothy, come fast and stop worrying about it. And don't stop. Keep going. See if you can come again. This time see how *fast* you can come. And then do it a third time. Get Dorothy involved. Let her know what you want to do . . . come as many times in a single afternoon or evening as it's humanly possible. Get her to help you with that second and third (and fourth and fifth and whatever) erection. I bet you won't come fast after the first time or two."

Psychologists might call this suggestion *paradoxical intention*. This is a process of behavior modification that says you can change your attitude about a problem if you deliberately put yourself into a situation you've been anxious about or currently avoiding. I think it's related to Zen, and "going with." It's that old cliché, "If you can't lick 'em, join 'em." Don't fight it, go with the flow.

The moral of this story is that some liabilities (bad habits) actually may serve as assets.

Boredom is another example. Being bored is a terrific asset. Because it opens up a whole bunch of things you can do. Once you notice that you are bored, you may choose to continue being bored. Or you may think up something new to do that could move you into participation and intense excitement.

The same thing may be said about not enjoying sex for a hundred other reasons. Angela told me, "Not only do I not enjoy sex (intercourse), it's gotten so that I don't enjoy affection or holding and kissing, or anything that might lead to sex or suggest a sexual encounter."

The first time I see a client, I ask him or her to make a tape, following some guidelines that allow them to describe their current problem while explaining some of their sexual past. I do this for several reasons. (And I'll return to Angela in a moment . . . she's the perfect example of everything I'm about to say.)

First, I figure people talk a lot. I see this—that is, I hear it—all around me every day. Constantly mouths are moving and information is being transferred. But I notice that most of us never really, truly get a chance to *listen to ourselves*. And what a shame. So I ask people to make an audio cassette and I tell them to listen to it over and over and over.

Often people will tell a machine things they'd never tell any human. I also figured they'd be pretty truthful if they knew that their partners would never hear the tapes. (When I counsel couples, this is the understanding.)

Who could benefit most from this honesty? I asked myself. Why, the client, of course. When the client comes in with the tape, I ask if he or she listened to it. Most say yes, several times. And then I ask them to listen again, and this time listen for the assets. I tell them to forget about all the rules and listen for behavior that worked.

Angela's tape was just loaded with assets. I'm going to reproduce some of it here and comment in the margins next to the assets.

ASSET: She knows what affection *feels* like.	I've always been an affectionate person. My parents were affectionate people and I was brought up in a loving atmosphere. But now I am afraid to have affection

shown to me. I still need it. But I'm to the point where my husband is very unhappy, because he has needs as well.

I was young when Kenny and I met, we went through high school together, we learned about sex together. We started, you know, touching at maybe fourteen, fifteen, and we had sex almost daily after that. By sex I mean we petted, we brought each other to orgasm by touching and by rubbing against each other. We never had intercourse. I was afraid of getting pregnant, and my parents told me good girls didn't do that before they got married.

ASSET: She knows what orgasm feels like.

Recently I feel sex got to be too much work. During my high school years I was a gymnast and I was very strong. Kenny was also. He would stimulate himself by rubbing against my stomach and I would stimulate myself to the point of orgasm. As we got older and I wasn't in such good shape, I got tired of doing that. It did get to be an awful lot of work to be a contortionist or try to stimulate myself until it was enjoyable to me. And I didn't think it was exactly fair.

ASSET: She's bored.

I felt at the same time that my husband had needs and desires to be fulfilled and I always felt that I should never refuse him, and I didn't want him to ever feel that I didn't want him, so I tried to never say no. I did that as long as I could and I still do that, but my husband senses

ASSET: Like boredom, lack of communication presents choices. Are they going to start leveling or not?

that I'm certainly not enjoying it and that it isn't really the same thing for him, because he doesn't have the fulfillment and the pleasure of knowing that I'm enjoying the relationship as much as he is. I think he also feels a little threatened sometimes, as men sometimes do, because he feels that I'm not attracted to him, or he's not desirable to me.

We feel the sex problem is contaminating the rest of the relationship. My doctor suggested we go to a sex seminar at the university and we did, but after that we just used what we learned against each other. We got very defensive.

ASSET: She can make a similar decision now.

My parents were against Kenny because I didn't date any other people. I got the feeling my mother didn't really want me to date at all. I was forbidden to see him at one point. I decided that they were wrong and I would make my own decisions, and from that point I did.

A lot of friends said we weren't right, that we wouldn't be happy. And I couldn't accept it. It went on for three or four years and I wonder if somehow, somewhere in my mind if I didn't really wonder if they were right and I was wrong. Maybe I'm wondering now, I don't know.

Except for Kenny I didn't have any sexual experience until about a year ago when I traveled for the company I work

ASSET: Now she can do sex well, if she wishes.

ASSET: All body systems go.

ASSET: She can create a productive fantasy.

for to Europe. I do this twice a year. The first time was terrible. I was alone and I didn't really like it, but I found out things I didn't know I could do and I survived. The second trip I realized I better learn to do this well. I figured I'd do as much as possible to enjoy the trip, make it as interesting and meaningful as I could. The second trip I enjoyed very much and met a person who was interested in me sexually, and I found I was getting very turned on. I wasn't getting turned on at home. I was beginning to wonder if I could be turned on, and this experience at least told me that I could turn on. So physiologically I was normal. There was just something in my head keeping me from having those experiences at home with Kenny.

I had a dream recently. I woke up feeling very sexy. It felt good. I was turned on, really turned on, and I liked it. I held on to that feeling all day long. I thought about my dream. I didn't get much work done that day, and that evening when Kenny went to the YMCA I decided to try masturbation. I hadn't done that in a long, long time. I fantasized about my dreams and I used a vibrator and I masturbated to orgasm, and it made me feel very good. The next day I did it twice.

You see, people like Angela think their situation is hopeless, and the truth is, it is. And hopeless is never hope empty but is on the way to hopemore and hopefull. There are always assets waiting to be rediscovered and used well.

For example, I noticed that Angela was able to create a "productive fantasy." She didn't know it, but the moment she revealed that to herself, and recognized it for what it was, she was home free. For this was a key to her happiness.

I wondered if Angela might be agreeable to holding on to that dream a little longer and masturbating with Kenny present. Maybe at first in the dark, explaining it to him and then just knowing he was there, feeling his presence. I suggested that later they might want to try it again with some subdued lighting, or by candlelight, and in time perhaps Angela would let Kenny "touch her" to orgasm while she held the same dream. At the same time, I suggested that if Kenny isn't in Angela's dream already, perhaps she might slowly introduce him. Eventually Kenny will be in her dream (fantasy) and making love to her physically as well. It works that way. Honest.

Some psychologists call this "shaping," or "successive approximation," which is an acknowledged operant-conditioning process designed to allow the client to learn new behavior by reinforcing the existing behavior that most closely resembles the desired goal. I still say it's "going with."

Whatever works, works. And what doesn't work, doesn't work. And when something doesn't work, you try something else.

> If you believe,
>   feel,
>   think, and
>   act as if it will work . . .
>   it could.

If you believe,
    feel,
    think,
    and act as if it is working . . .
    it is.

The past is dead, use it well. The future lies ahead.

CHAPTER

8

Your Future Sex: Create a Productive Fantasy

"You know what I do?" the General Motors assembly-line worker said to a writer from *True* magazine. "I fit seven bolts. Seven bolts! Day in and day out, the same seven bolts. You know what I think about? Raquel Welch."

A bored housewife talks about what it's like to make beds and go shopping and cook and clean up, day after day after day. She daydreams about Robert Redford.

For some people, this is about as far as fantasy goes. And it seems harmless. There's nothing really dangerous or weird about imagining sexual intimacy with a popular movie star, or athlete, or even (in the days of American Camelot) a president. The only thing is, however much fun it may be, and diverting, it doesn't "really" accomplish much.

To be sure, it keeps Raquel Welch and Robert Redford and several others in the list of top ten box-office champs and it wins votes in the November elections, but what does this sort of fantasy do for those who have it? It helps, it helps, the fantasizers say, and I'm certain that it does. But sexual fantasy could do so much more. There was a rock band back in the sixties called Steppenwolf (named for the Hermann Hesse novel), whose first hit song was called "Magic Carpet Ride." One of the lines from the song proclaimed: "Fantasy will set you free."

How true that can be, if only fantasy is given a chance. The odd thing is, sexual fantasy has been given a bad time of it over the years. The writings of Krafft-Ebing and Sigmund Freud, and the infamous Marquis de Sade, are rich in sexual fantasy. However, rather than consider the possible positive side of such imagining, these men, and others, have focused only on deviant behavior. Some have gone so far as to issue warnings that link masturbatory fantasy with a long list of aberrant activities. By masturbating over a long period to mental pictures of small children, for example, a potential child molester is supposed to evolve.

For some people, that may be true. It may also be true that for many people sexual fantasy may serve as a "safety valve" for releasing bottled-up sexual frustrations that are antisocial or unacceptable to the physical or mental welfare of the individual or his (or her) sex partner. It was Freud's opinion that sexual fantasy was no more than a negative response to frustration.

I believe that these conclusions (theories?) are firmly stuck in the Leftsidedness of sexual fantasy. For others— for those who want it so—sexual fantasy can be a powerful moving force, a tool as valuable to the average man and woman as the brush is to the painter.

This tool might also be regarded as a game, called Create a Productive Fantasy, or Up Your Orgasm. Like all successful games, it's easy to play and fun. Unlike most other games, however, in Up Your Orgasm, everyone wins.

FANTASY WILL SET YOU FREE

Not everyone is against sexual fantasy. Jerome Singer, director of the graduate program in clinical psychology at Yale, wrote in *Psychology Today* that "Fantasies and daydreams, far from being irrelevant and insubstantial (another popular point of view), may be the foundation of serenity and purpose in our lives." Unimaginative people, he said, became easily bored and were less relaxed and independent than highly imaginative people.

Unimaginative people, he said, ". . . want autonomy but have little sense of the planning and slow achievement that might win them real personal freedom. Lacking the ability to try out, in fantasy and with impunity, a range of possibilities, they seem to be the victims of external forces . . . whether drugs, or sights and sounds, or other people. They lack the inner control and quiet sense of purpose that a rich imagination can provide."

The noted sexologists, Drs. Phyllis and Eberhard Kronhausen, agree. They wrote in *Erotic Fantasies: A Study of the Sexual Imagination* that it is sexual fantasy "that distinguishes human sexuality from that of the lower species. We have little cause, therefore, to be either afraid or ashamed of our sex fantasies, as aberrant, deviant, and bizarre as they may be. The more intelligent the individual, the greater the role of fantasy in his sex life. This does not mean that he (or she) will be governed by sex fantasies to the exclusion of social sex contacts and intense involvement with real (nonimagined) sex partners. But it does mean that a free fantasy life will contribute to creative thinking, whereas mental blocks or inhibitions will interfere with the creative process."

The key word is "creative." For to be able to fantasize is to have the ability to form mental representations of things not actually present—an abstract and highly creative act. Now we get into levels of creativity. Granted, sexual fantasy can be fun and diverting and sometimes (usually with masturbation) a sort of make-do substitute for the Real Thing. But, really, how creative is that?

If the Kronhausens and Singer opened the door, two other doctors from Stanford University, Herant A. Katchadourian and Donald T. Lunde, stuck their foot inside. In their excellent survey, *Fundamentals of Human Sexuality*, they said ". . . some fantasies revolve around future events and can sometimes be of very definite help in real-life situations. As an individual anticipates problems, plans for contingencies, and mentally rehearses alternative modes of action, such a person lessens anxiety and prepares to cope with novel situations. There is thus a difference between fantasies that substitute for action and those that prepare for it."

Permit me to repeat that final sentence: *There is thus a difference between fantasies that substitute for action and those that prepare for it.*

It is possible through fantasy to leave Leftsidedness alone and step into the future, to experience the excitation of Rightsidedness through imaging (which is one of the things that the right hemisphere of the brain is so good at). That is what "creating a productive fantasy" means— putting sexual fantasy to work. Using it to gain the future the individual (or couple) wants.

HOW TO RECOGNIZE A PRODUCTIVE FANTASY WHEN YOU SEE ONE

In 1960 in Rome a tall, thin black man from Ethiopia, Abebe Bikila, ran the Olympic marathon (barefoot) and won. He did so again in 1964, in Tokyo, setting a record that stands today. In 1977 I saw a movie starring Dustin Hoffman, *The Marathon Man*. On a wall in his New York apartment is a poster of Bikila, and during one of the film's most suspenseful scenes Hoffman is fleeing on foot from armed gunmen. Suddenly the film adopts Hoffman's point of view, and on the screen we see Hoffman's vision: a picture of Bikila crossing the marathon finish line. It spurs Hoffman on to greater speed and he eludes his deadly pursuers.

Was this a productive fantasy? You bet it was.

There was a novel published some years ago by the French writer Romain Gary, *The Roots of Heaven*. French prisoners in a German camp are demoralized until one of them moves a pretty but imaginary girl into their midst. Everyone agrees to treat her as a lady. Morale improves enormously, but the German commandant learns what's going on and, fancying himself a psychologist, he demands the prisoners give up their woman so she can be taken to a brothel for German officers. The men refuse, and the commandant knows he is defeated.

Fantasy is all around us, it's a part of our everyday life, and has been for thousands of years. Many people tell me they can't fantasize; they say they don't know how. But of course they do it all the time.

—A child asks the department store Santa Claus for a doll and a two-wheeler bike and for the next ten days imagines how wonderful it will be when she gets them.

—A housewife plans a dinner party for eight, fretting over the menu, the seating arrangement, and what she'll wear.

—A farmer looks at the Sears, Roebuck catalog (called "the wish book" in earlier times) and orders a smoking jacket. Back in town, where the Sears warehouse is, someone else is reading *The Whole Earth Catalog*, dreaming about a return to the land.

—A skinny high school male looks at a picture of Arnold Schwarzenegger, the current Mr. Universe.

—A working girl has just weighed herself and is now standing nude in front of a full-length mirror, vowing to begin a diet the following day.

—A young man turns the pages of his address book, planning his weekend dating forays, weighing this one and then that one before making the telephone call.

—A woman who believes her breasts are small opens her husband's subscription copy of PLAYBOY to the centerfold and wonders what if.

—Her husband looks at the same picture and wonders too.

—An elderly couple on Social Security orders a brochure for a round-the-world tour from a travel agency.

—A man in his forties looks at the Mercedes-Benz through the showroom window.

How many of these fantasies were "productive"? How many could be? Notice that everyone fantasizes *all the time*. Why not make *all* fantasies productive? Why not put them all to work?

DON'T MAKE IT TOO DIFFICULT

The first kind of fantasy not to have is a fantasy with Raquel Welch or Robert Redford, unless, of course, you're married to them. That may seem harmless, but it really is just an exercise in frustration. It is like wishing you could reach an orgasm *tonight*. Or setting as a goal for today a full half hour of intercourse before ejaculation when so far, in 25 or 30 years of life, the best you've done is three minutes. That's setting your sights too high.

Remember the man who said about his erection problem, "During all the time that I've had this problem, the way I would handle it was to try to ignore it and hope that somehow magically it would go away"? His fantasy demanded magic.

Another man came to me complaining of diminished sexual activity. He said of his relationship with his wife, "I saw my appetite wane. What was even more disturbing was the prospect that there would come a day when it would no longer bother me that I had no sexual feeling or desire for my wife. As anticipated, that day actually did come." Of course it did. The Broadway and film producer David Merrick jokingly introduced his wife for years as "the future ex-Mrs. Merrick"; was it any wonder that they divorced? These doomsayers recall something Emerson wrote: "Beware of what you want, for you will get it."

The ones daydreaming of Raquel Welch; the ones waiting for magical cures, or pretending nothing is wrong; the ones engaged in self-fulfilling prophecy—all of these people share one thing. They are setting themselves up for failure. Their fantasies are neither creative nor productive. In fact, they are counterproductive. The owners of such fantasies cannot win.

MAKE IT EASY INSTEAD

A woman came to me and said she didn't know how to fantasize, swore by all that was holy that she'd never had one, not since she was a little girl and believed in the Easter Bunny and Santa Claus. I smiled at her image and suggested she close her eyes. "Where were you this morning?" I asked her.

She said she was at home. "Good," I said, "can you describe the house for me, describe the room you were in?"

She did so. "Now," I said, "tell me what time it is.

What are you doing? What's the weather like outside?"

She answered each question clearly and quickly and soon was beginning to elaborate those answers with rich detail.

"Stop," I said. "Open your eyes. That's a fantasy. You're not there."

The woman looked puzzled. I suggested that if she could get a picture from her past, couldn't she also get a picture from her future? She still seemed puzzled. But ever hopefull.

"This is an easy process," I said. "It really is. Mentally, get a file folder and get a picture of when you were born, at least a date, and whatever else you've been told about your birth, and put it in the file. Now get a second file folder and put in it a picture of the first thing you consciously remember. Get another file and mark it 'First Day of School.' Keep going all the way up to the present time. This year's file will be thicker than the one for the year of your birth because you remember more. But now that you have your life organized, you'll have pictures that go all the way back. Now you can pull out the pictures you want and look at them, one at a time. Unless there is flypaper in the file and the pictures start sticking together. For example, when you pull out a picture from 1977 and it's stuck to a picture from 1936. That's okay, of course, if it serves you well. But if you were sexually molested when you were five years old in 1936 and that picture is stuck to last night's picture when you were out on a date and afraid again of being molested, well, it's time to clean up your file and get the flypaper out.

"Now, having said all that," I told the woman in my office, "could you get a file going that says June, even though it's only January now? Could you create a picture of what you'll be doing in six months? No? Well, notice that as we've been talking, two minutes have passed. It's no longer eleven-fifteen, it's eleven-seventeen. Can you picture eleven-nineteen? Can you imagine getting up two minutes from now to get a glass of water? Get a picture of the glass. Be very specific. Got it? Good. Now in two minutes, do it. That's creating a fantasy and then acting on it. Once you start practicing games like this, you're moving into your own future."

For example, I really put it to my son Jeffrey yesterday morning. I said, "Jeffrey, I acknowledge your sister Dana as being the worst imaginable sister you could possibly have. I give that to you. You've created it. Now, I want you to make-believe that you can be nice to her. I don't want toleration in this household. I can't stand it, Jeffrey, I don't want people in this house who don't give a damn. I don't want you tolerating your sister Dana anymore. I want you to start playing a role. I want you to practice it every day. How can you do things for your sister? How can you make her feel good? Even though I acknowledge that you're absolutely right about her being the worst sister imaginable." And then I said the same thing to Dana about Jeffrey.

I tell all the people who come to me with sex problems the same thing I told my kids yesterday morning: "I don't want any faking! I want rehearsal!"

SOME GOOD REHEARSALS

Every one of the most common sexual complaints may be countered at least in part with productive fantasy, so I ask all of the people who see me to create one—to tell me exactly what it is they want.

I ask everyone to "fantasize for a moment what the ideal sexual relationship would be for you? Where are you? What time is it? Who are you with? What is happening? How does it end?"

The fantasies I hear are wonderful.

Here's one from a woman who thought sex was dirty and who really hated doing it (remember Buffy?):

> It is evening time and I am with my husband. Maybe we're just lying together on the deck of a ship, or sitting together in the sand, or running down the beach. Things like that mean a lot to me. Just tender touching. Not a mind wandering on what's happening in business. Just tender looking. Tender caressing, I guess. I feel sex is a tender thing, I want it to be the gentlest thing possible.

Here's an I-come-too-fast fantasy:

> The best relationships I've ever had with my wife have been in hotel rooms. She claims it's because she is out of the routine, she is more receptive. So that's the first thing . . . a trip to one of the neighbor islands, a deluxe hotel room. I'm not too particular about the time, but some of the most exciting times I've had with my wife have been after we've both had something to drink. I also enjoy sex during the day. My wife is less tired at that time and I enjoy the visual aspects. I enjoy seeing her in the nude. I like to enjoy a wide variety of sexual experiences. I enjoy long foreplay. I remember when we were first married she'd say, "Wouldn't you like to put Herman in?" Obviously once I've had a climax my enthusiasm dwindles noticeably, so I've come to like the foreplay to run thirty minutes, forty-five minutes, an hour maybe. My wife is capable of having multiple climaxes, so in my fantasy I'd bring her to at least two, one during foreplay, the other during intercourse, after I put "Herman" in.

This is the fantasy of someone with herpes:

My lover and I are hugging, kissing, touching, laughing. I see me making him come with my hands and mouth, making him feel good. And then he's doing the same to me. Then I see him entering me without any pain and just making love in any number of positions. I don't see any particular positions, just doing whatever comes naturally. What mainly is happening, though, is the total love feeling, the energy vibrations, me feeling that things are being done to me and moving freely when I feel the good feelings. And making sounds come out, and nothing feels like it's behind, held back. Where none of that old junk comes in . . . all of that shit that I keep having go through my mind and my body. None of that is happening. We are just being.

Now that's a terrific fantasy. Notice, by the way, that these fantasies all have involved the problemed person's partner. There are other fantasies which do not have the partners in them, but draw upon a wide assortment of old boy friends and old girl friends, people at work, even strangers. Jerome had been married for seven and a half years, and although he hadn't ever had sex with anyone other than his wife, he wasn't sleeping with her either. He was, in a word, bored. This was his fantasy:

I'm on the bus and it's in the evening on the way back from work and I'm by myself. There are three or four nice-looking chicks sitting around within viewing distance. Everybody's being with themselves except this one nice-looking blonde with blue eyes. She looks up and smiles at me. I smile back at her. She turns and comes back and sits down with me. We strike up a conversation and she says to me: "How'd you like to go to bed?" I say, "You know I'm married." And she says, "Sure, hell . . ." And I say, "Great, you got your own place?" And she says, "Fine, yep, I do, how about right now?" I say, "Great." And we get off the bus and go over to her place. I'm really nervous about it, but we go in and we sit on the couch and start passionately kissing. Passionately passionate. Her hands slide down around my waist and in between my legs and she starts to rub my penis. She starts to moan. She gets really hot. I put my hand between her legs and . . .

. . . I feel the muscles inside of her vagina pressing against my penis as it goes in and out. She's laying there, she's breathing as hard as she possibly can. And moaning. I just keep on going at it and going at it and going at it, until finally I feel some jerking motion inside of her and see that she's in absolute ecstasy, she's having an orgasm. So I start to pump faster and I start to have an orgasm with her. I feel the sides of her walls crushing in on me. Jesus Christ, it's just unbelievable. The way it ends . . . just absolute relief, both of us just laying there, still a part of one another, kissing and hugging and talking about the next time we'll get together again. (Laughter) Yessss. That's my idea of a fantasy for you.

Some obviously have a more vivid, or detailed, imagination than others. This is most helpful, and more about that in a moment. First, the fantasies of two bored, non-orgasmic women whose partners are absent from their fantasies, too:

I fantasize about a man that we both know. He lives in San Francisco, he's Armenian, he's dark, he has a mustache. He's very masculine looking. He's very nice, he seems to be very enthusiastic about life and very happy, and he has a nice way with women. I suppose I think about going there by myself or with a girl friend and me dropping in where he works saying hello. He asks me out to dinner that night and we go to dinner and enjoy ourselves thoroughly. Then he invites me over to his place, and the rest just naturally takes place. It just ends in a very satisfying relationship, where we're both satisfied after having sexual intercourse and that's it. I don't see us going any farther than that, or us becoming serious or me wanting a divorce or anything like that. I just see myself enjoying, enjoying, enjoying someone else and still staying married. I see myself having this other man for strictly sexual satisfaction.

I'm in some kind of meadow where there are trees and flowers and high grass and the sun is just going down. It's between light and darkness, where everything is soft and shadowed. Normally I enjoy having sex much more in the dark. I'm there with Rick, who is the guy that I had this one sexual experience with. We're running through the tall grass playing hide-and-seek and tag and laughing and giggling. It's in a place where nobody can find us. There's no fear of being discovered. The sun is beginning to set. Finally we just fall down in the grass and we start kissing, hugging, caressing. And then we get undressed. There's no time consideration. We can take as long as we want. We kiss and laugh and hug and finally we start to have oral sex and we do that for a while. I'm getting excited. He penetrates me. Together we go back and forth and I come while he is in me and then he comes. The two of us just stay there for a while like that, and fall asleep in each other's arms.

MAKING FANTASY REAL: PUTTING IT TO WORK

For some people, fantasy involves the suspension of belief. They say to accept something like Santa Claus or Walt Disney's talking dogs and ducks and mice you *have* to abandon reality. I recognize that point of view. But I believe that it is just as valid to regard fantasies as real, rather than a pleasant hoax. The way to make them real, of course, is to put the lovely little things to work for you.

For example, a legal secretary named Beverly said she was unable to experience orgasm with her husband, although she told me that she could do so alone. I suggested that she might continue to masturbate and when she neared the moment of orgasm she might begin to imagine that her partner was in the room with her. This would allow her partner to come close to her, in fantasy, at her most intimate moment. And that might be as much as she might wish to try to achieve in the first session.

In the second session of self-stimulation, I suggested, she might now wish to carry the fantasy a step farther and permit her fantasy partner to substitute his fingers for her own. And in the third session Beverly was urged to allow her partner's penis to take the place of his hand. I assured her that there needn't be any actual insertion yet; the fantasized penis would remain outside, massaging the vaginal lips and clitoris. As before, with this fantasy in mind, Beverly was to stimulate herself to orgasm. For the fourth session, I suggested that Beverly's fantasy might be extended to involve her partner's beginning sexual intercourse at the moment she climaxed manually.

Then I told Beverly that after she'd had these "warm-up" sessions (rehearsals), she might repeat each step, masturbating with her partner actually present, making her fantasies come true by involving him as orgasm approached. I assured her that she could feel awkward about masturbating in her partner's presence initially. I pointed out that many, many couples stimulated themselves when together, often continuing this activity to climax. At first, Beverly was reluctant to do this, but soon she realized that there really were no rules in sex, so long as everyone was responsible.

"Besides," I said, "how else is Ted going to know exactly what turns you on most unless you show him?"

Beverly followed the suggested chronology perfectly until she got to step three, where Ted was supposed to refrain from sexual intercourse. He couldn't hold back and she couldn't hold back and she experienced orgasm with her partner, ahead of schedule.

Others have accelerated the program in the same way, accomplishing their goal of orgasm-during-intercourse in as few as one or two sessions. Some seem to have gotten over much of the problem *just by hearing Beverly's story*.

Psychologists sometimes call the process I used with Beverly *masturbatory conditioning*. This is a procedure based on classical (Pavlovian) conditioning principles, where in this instance the person learns to associate orgasm with her partner's graduated participation. It is important to notice that in each session, Beverly rewarded herself for including her partner in her fantasy. And what did she do to reward herself? She gave herself an orgasm, which is the most positive reinforcing event available to a human. There is nothing in the human experience that *feels* better. So anything you associate with orgasm is probably going to feel good, too.

Remember the two kinds of fantasy—the ones involving the client's partner, and the ones involving others? They really aren't far apart. If you're troubled about not experiencing orgasm with your partner, or reaching it too fast, and your ideal sexual fantasy includes your partner, you're already on the road to resolution. If your fantasy involves someone other than your partner, you are only slightly farther down the same road. It is just a matter of transferring your partner's face (and whatever) to the one in your present fantasy, and then as before, turning fantasy into reality by introducing the Real Thing (your partner).

It works. Even in the more unusual cases it works. Colin said he was a "driven homosexual," and that his midnight cruising of the city's gay baths was destroying a marriage he wished to preserve. (His wife worked at night, which gave him this freedom of movement.) Also, loss of sleep was causing him to fall behind at work.

"Guilt is my middle name," he said. As it happened, his fantasy was a lovely one . . . calling for him to please and satisfy his wife as well as himself, heterosexually. I suggested that it was okay to have homosexual relations if he wanted to, and maybe the next time he might wish to get a picture of that fantasy, get a picture of satisfying his wife and himself through intercourse at the moment he reached a climax with another male. "No matter how it happens, through fellatio or by hand or anally, whatever it is you do," I said, "when you come, get a picture of doing that with your wife." He did and in less than a month he stopped his midnight cruising. An 18-month follow-up confirmed the productive fantasy's effectiveness.

In another case, a man regarded himself as a potential child molester. He said that when he masturbated he had fantasies of girls between six and ten. I said, "Great, keep it up, but the next time you masturbate, make her twelve. I don't want to see you. Just call me when she's twelve." He called and I told him to do it again, and this time make her 14 and give her some adolescent breasts and the start of some pubic hair. And so it went, until he was stimulating himself to a fantasy woman of 21. He then went out and initiated a relationship with a woman of that age.

BE SPECIFIC ABOUT WHAT YOU WANT

Some of the fantasies excerpted in this chapter are extremely detailed. They are the best kind. The characters you remember in books (or movies) are the ones whose personalities are best defined. In situations that you remember well, you can probably remember the color of the walls, the weather, the clothes you were wearing, even the smells you smelled. So make your fantasies vivid, personal, detailed.

Where are you? Are you on a beach, in a hotel room, or running through tall grass, as some of the productive daydreamers in this chapter? When it comes time to make fantasy real, the proper setting could be the factor that makes fantasy reality.

What time is it? A fantasy that takes place at sunset will become reality most easily at approximately the same time.

What is happening? Are the kids asleep or somewhere else, giving you the freedom you want? Is there a romantic meal, is there some good wine? Do you talk first? What, specifically, do you say to your partner? Who makes the first move? What happens first? What happens next?

The idea is that if the fantasy is "almost real," the transfer to reality will be easier. How many of us have been awakened from deep sleep by a dream so vivid that we say it was the dream that woke us up? Creating a productive fantasy is creating *that* kind of dream—a daydream so real it wakes us up.

GIVE YOURSELF A ROUND OF APPLAUSE

A final thing to notice is the wisdom and usefulness of self-congratulations. Never, ever be reluctant to applaud yourself for taking even the smallest step toward your goal. Always notice that you took that step, then give yourself a hand.

Right from the start, people want acknowledgment: "Look, ma, no hands! Look, daddy, look at me!" It never stops. We want acknowledgment (validation) throughout life. This need drives some men to become president, some women to become movie stars. Most people settle for a casual but sincere "Nice job, Harry" in the office (and maybe a bonus check) or a warm "Oh, you lost weight, you look good" from the girl friend. Those are terrific rewards.

Self-applause is even better. When you start putting your fantasy to work, acknowledge yourself with a big smile and say, "I did it." There is nothing better for building a sense of self-worth. If you want to be accepted by others, first you must accept yourself. It's like my son Jeff coming home and saying, "I got an A." If he did that, I'd say, "How'd it make you feel?" Notice that. Instead of "I think that's terrific, son," I say, "How'd it make you feel?" I don't want Jeff to get good grades for *me*. If he chooses to get them at all, I want him to get them for *himself*.

It works the same way in finding sexual contentedness. You get a picture and figure out when you can do it. That day, that evening, the next morning, whenever. Then do it. Then get the next picture. But also say, "Wow, I did it!"

What'd you do?

"I took the first step."

You bet you did, and that's great. Get ready for the second.

It's not just strokes from others that you get. More important are the strokes you give yourself, the "I-did-it's." People will notice. And then, *that'll* be an extra.

A piece of one more fantasy. "How does it end?" I asked, and the answer came: "I know how I'd feel at the end . . . like a giant smile button, extremely satisfied with myself and thinking I'm pretty magnificent."

Now there's someone who has learned to play Up Your Orgasm well.

CHAPTER

9

Introducing: The
Could-Be Cleopatra
and Casanova Tapes

When Dr. William Masters and Virginia Johnson published their landmark book, *Human Sexual Inadequacy*, they defined sexual inadequacy to include anybody who had not achieved sexual communication in marriage, or who did not feel secure with what sexual communication he or she had. They estimated that half of all married couples in the United States probably qualified.

Although nearly a decade has passed since the book's publication, and sex research, sex training, sex education, and sex therapy programs are blooming profusely around the country, the 50 percent figure likely hasn't diminished much. There still are millions upon millions of couples—married and unmarried—who remain stuck in Leftsidedness, who are less than content in bed.

The following ten chapters show how others who once were stuck in Leftsidedness and no longer are (or are on their way to being unstuck) negotiated from left to right and found (or are now on their way to finding) the satisfaction they were seeking so anxiously. You have read many of the "I-knew-a-person-once . . ." stories already. Here now are more. Here are their stories, told in their words, taken from the audio tapes they made following our first meeting.

Perhaps a few words about how I came to use audio tapes might be helpful. The first step might have been my seeing a production (at UCLA) of Samuel Beckett's *Krapp's Last Tape*. This was a one-act play, the sensation of the Off-Broadway season in 1960, that made shattering drama out of the monologue of a man who, after 30 years, plays back an autobiographical tape he recorded on his thirty-ninth birthday. Krapp, now 69, hears his own description of a day in a small boat on a lake when he put his face against a woman's breasts. It was a glorious moment for Krapp, but then he began to make a new tape, saying he'd "just been listening to that stupid bastard I took myself for, thirty years ago; hard to believe I was ever as bad as that."

Krapp wasn't noticing his assets. But within moments he turned 180 degrees and ran the old tape back and listened to the day on the lake again, absolutely entranced. Now that long-ago experience took on all the enjoyable trappings of fantasy. If Samuel Beckett had written a second act, it might have shown how Krapp turned that fantasy into reality.

About the same time I saw this play, the group sessions with Josh Golden (and the pregnant women) were organized, and we began to tape some of them—using reel-to-reel tapes in those precassette days. We listened to the pregnant women's tapes over and over again as we wrote up our findings for a medical journal. This is how successful persons and tapes became linked for me, and when I began counseling in Seattle I started using both as a learning aid.

Somewhere along the line I learned that nearly all troubled people benefit (feel better at least, maybe think better and do better, too) from hearing that someone else has the same or a similar problem. So nowadays when people come to me, usually sometime during the first visit, I play a portion of one of these tapes, selecting the appropriate tape for the person sitting with me, according to what his or her complaint may be. All report some comfort from hearing even the tiniest portion of the selected tape. Some get so much benefit that the next thing I know the person is calling to cancel all further meetings because the problem has gone or is going away, or is no longer regarded as a problem.

You may, therefore, feel some relief just by reading the chapters that follow. You may also find that your problem and your perception of it is changing as you read. You may even move from Leftsidedness to Rightsidedness merely by turning a dozen or so pages.

Of course instant satisfaction doesn't come to everyone. (Some people learn faster than others, and that's okay.) For most of us, it is necessary to practice, practice, practice. No matter how long or short the process (and it always seems long when it isn't immediate), satisfaction comes and comes and comes. If you have readiness, purposefullness, and hopefullness, if you don't get stuck and don't let your liabilities get in the way of your assets, and if you can create a productive fantasy.

It's that easy.

THE DIDS, DIDN'TS, AND COULDS

The case histories that follow are from my files; the words are from the actual tapes my clients made when they came for counseling, and they are the same tapes I've played for other clients when *they* came in. You will notice that in all these case histories I have interrupted the tape transcripts with my own parenthetical remarks, creating a sort of artificial dialogue with each of the individuals. These are comments which occurred to me as I listened to the tapes. Later, when I met the individuals a second time, I shared these observations with them—pointing out what I call *dids*, *didn'ts*, and *coulds*.

—"Dids," of course, are assets—things that have worked in the past. A woman who says she cannot reach orgasm at all these days, for example, may report that she *did* experience sexual climax with a college sweetheart once, or through masturbation when she was a teen-ager. Similarly, a man complaining of erection failure may not always have had that problem. And so on. "Dids" are the sexual "good old days" and they may be used to bring back those good old days once they are noticed.

—"Didn'ts" are the liabilities, the things that didn't work. Very often people with sexual complaints are stuck in this category of behavior. In fact, just about all they notice are the "didn'ts." So when Shirley didn't come last night, she assumes she won't come again tonight . . . and the same goes for Harry with his erection woes.

—"Coulds" are the options and choices available, the glorious possibilities. "Coulds" are items that worked once ("dids") and for one reason or another have not been tried for a while, but *could* be tried again. "Coulds" are things that others have tried and found successful, things that other sexual losers *could* try. "Coulds" are fantasies that get you out of the woods (or "woulds": I could if I would).

As you read the transcripts you will notice that many of them have been sprinkled liberally with precisely this kind of interruption. Sometimes when I see a client a second time I play back part of his or her tape and stop it just as I have here, offering an observation. I may do the same when I play the tape for others with the same problem, saying something like, "Did you notice what you (that person) said? That's a 'didn't'—something that *didn't* work . . ."

For example, Buddy complained that he couldn't get it up.

> Although I feel I have a desire for my wife, I am afraid that I will not be able to complete the performance and will not be able to satisfy myself or my wife. (*Worry is rehearsal for failure. He's setting himself up. Worry never makes a penis hard—it often guarantees that it will be soft. Worry is always a "didn't." It also might be called a "can't."*)

For another example, Stella said she wasn't able to experience orgasm.

> I used to have sexual fantasies a lot. I remember having them, quite a few, as a teen-ager. But I threw every sexual fantasy away. I think it goes back to the fact that I would massively repress all my sexual thoughts, just put them way in the back of my head. Even when I had a sexual orgasm I'd just throw it into the back of my head and forget it. (*This short paragraph is full of assets and liabilities, packed with "dids" that Stella has turned into "didn'ts" or "won'ts." Once upon a nicer time she had sexual fantasies, and now, if she wishes, she may again. Once upon a nicer time she had orgasms, and now if she wishes she may have them again, too. The "dids" she turned into "didn'ts" may now become "coulds."*)

Essentially, the transcripts which follow have caught the sexual loser in the *"before"* stage. My parenthetical remarks show some of the early steps the clients may take if they wish. The *"after"* picture follows the transcripts.

Here I offer further remarks, spell out what, specifically, was suggested and done, and what it got the client: a move from left to right, change from sexual loserdom to sexual winnerdom.

Some chose to make their failing marriages/partnerships begin to work. Others had experienced too much (for them) pain already even to consider this possibility. So in some cases the partnerships ended. Sometimes that's the way it is in winning. The point is: *all these one-time losers are now winners.*

Keep in mind as you read about these wonderful people that they are not exceptional (except in the sense that we are all exceptional) and that their stories are representative of the complaints they are now verbalizing. By reading these stories, and noticing the assets and liabilities (the *dids*, *didn'ts*, and *coulds*), and by noticing readiness, purposefullness, and hopefullness, perhaps you may notice such things in your own life. Acquisitions or "coulds" may occur to you. They did to many as they listened.

You may also notice that some of the complaints that follow overlap, that many of the individuals really have two or three or more related complaints. This, too, is typical. Many of the men who experience an erection problem also sometimes experience what they call "premature ejaculation," and that, in turn, has nurtured the so-called impotence due to a *fear of performance*, which is so common in many of the most common sexual complaints. As noted in an earlier chapter, a man with an erection problem also may be partnered with a woman with dyspareunia. And a man's "soft-on" or a woman's failure to experience orgasm may be related to anyone's (and possibly everyone's) boredom in the bedroom; thus "I can't keep it up" and "I can't come vaginally" may be rooted in "I don't want to do it."

Additionally, some of the specific suggestions that worked for one complaint may be used to dissolve several others, yet to avoid repetition I have introduced it in this book with only one.

Clearly, it will serve everyone well to read *all* the case histories, even if some of the specific complaints don't seem at first to be relevant. Every once-was loser has something valuable to say to every would-be winner.

Of course, all identities have been disguised and names have been changed—as they have been throughout this book—to assure the individuals' privacy. The problems remain very real, and each of the losers-turned-winners would wish for you to use their experiences to your advantage.

Now it is my pleasure to introduce the people I knew once, and still remember . . . the best sex therapists in the world . . . people just like you . . . who were/are willing to try something new, who were/are getting full of intention (purpose) and hope (desire plus expectation), who were/are walking away from what didn't work and embracing whatever did, who were/are putting their once-dormant but now-fertile imaginations to work. Here, then, is American ingenuity in its finest hour . . .

Bedtime.

CHAPTER

10

"I Don't Feel Like Doing It"

The most obvious reason in cases of not "doing it"—or for any other complaint of sexual dissatisfaction, for that matter—has to be that he or she is not having any fun. I believe that these people have learned to be (think/feel/do) exactly the way they are and that if they are dissatisfied, then the first step is to describe what "satisfied" is. Next, these people may wish to see how it is possible to move from A to B, from dissatisfaction to satisfaction. To do this, they must notice the barriers to attainment. If there is a *deficit*—not enough erection, no orgasm, infrequency of intercourse, no fun, etc.—they may add a capacity. If there is an *excess*—too much guilt, pain, etc.—this may be left alone, and some new thinking/feeling/doing behavior may be learned.

Let's listen now and see/hear from the first sexual loser-turned-winner—and plan a learning experience.

ELISE

Elise married the first man she went to bed with, before she was 19. She had two children, a nice home, and she believed that her husband loved her, yet after ten years of marriage she "longed to be free and single again."

"We haven't had any sexual encounter for a month and a half now and I can't say I have any desire to have anything to do with my husband. (*How about with others?*) The way I understand it, your program is to improve the sexual relationship, but what I don't understand is how you can improve it when you don't have any desire to even do anything with the other person. Any affection he has toward me I seem to be resisting more. I should be trying more now, but it doesn't seem to come naturally. (*She's asking, "Don't I have to be motivated?" Sure, by you; and notice you're in my office!*)

"I felt there was a certain mystery about him when we started dating, but it wasn't mystery at all—he was introverted. (*How do you know this for certain? Maybe he really is mysterious. Besides, what's "introverted" mean?*) He doesn't go to people, they have to come to him. He doesn't get much out of life. He's a dull person to be around; there's something about him that's boring to me now. (*Asset: She's bored. That's a beginning. She could change. She could excite him!*) It wasn't always that way, but now he likes the routine, which I find boring. (*Asset: She remembers when it wasn't boring. She could re-create that.*) He's been doing the same things for nine years and it's gotten to me. (*Has she been doing different things for nine years? If not, what could she do?*)

"I enjoyed our sex before marriage, sometimes more than on the honeymoon, when I felt I had to force myself to do it. Sexual relations became better after we were married a few years, particularly when I was trying to get pregnant. When I was trying to get pregnant, there seemed to be a reason for doing it (*purposefull*). Now there doesn't seem to be any reason. (*Liability: She's limiting sex to the reproductive act. Only a few sexual acts are reproductive. She isn't including relational and recreational sex. Perhaps she's never yet experienced it. It also sounds like she's not experiencing orgasm during "sexual relations."*)

"Although I'm happy to have them, I feel sometimes the kids get in the way of myself and my husband. We're not able to enjoy one another in a perfectly relaxed atmosphere all the time, not even to have intercourse when we feel like it. (*She could go to sleep when the children did and wake up early or during the night, or get a sitter.*) They're always around, and things always seem to be so routine. Nothing comes natural anymore. (*Liability: She is using the word "natural" improperly. How can anything two creatures of nature do be unnatural? Besides that, are eyeglasses natural, are airplanes natural, is singing natural, is combing hair natural, is diapering natural?*)

"I wasn't ever taught about sex (*not yet*). I was given a book about menstrual periods. Intercourse wasn't spoken of. The only talk I had was with my mother when I was in one room and she was in another, and I had a couple of questions about having periods. And that's all. My parents never encouraged or discouraged anything as far as boys were concerned, except the hour I was to be in at night. (*She could, I hope, develop a different curriculum for her children.*)

"I had my first sexual encounter when I was sixteen, and I married Paul two years later. I don't feel I ever really entered into the actual feeling of intercourse. (*Yup, no big "O." No wonder she was bored.*) No feeling of contentment came out of it for me. (*Not even a little "o."*) I was more concerned about the possible results of the intercourse, of becoming pregnant, or just feeling guilty after doing something like that.

"I have been having more fantasies lately. It doesn't disturb me that I have these fantasies. If anything, it makes me want to have something in my own life that is actually really happening to me rather than just to dream about it. (*Asset: She could make these fantasies serve her well.*)

"I feel it'll be difficult to get it on with my husband because it's gone so far. (*Liability: This could turn into self-fulfilling prophecy.*) I have no interest now, but I don't want to get divorced. The kids and all, the hassle would be too much. What I really want is to learn how to fall in love with him all over again." (*Purposefullness: She knows what she wants. Elise's wish to learn how to fall in love with her husband again, or to be single again, which is when she fell in love with him in the first place, is no more than a wish to return to that space in her life where and when she viewed her husband, and sex, as exciting. She didn't know it, but that constituted a big "did" in her life, a terrific asset, which she could—and did—use well. One of the things I did, to assist her in recreating that sense of well-being, was give her an audio cassette reproduced below: "Learning self-stimulation."* My idea was to introduce her to orgasm, then get him involved in her successful fantasy, and finally have him involved in physical fact.*)

DR.:   Hello, I'm Dr. Ron Pion and I'm pleased to have this opportunity to talk with you. For many women who have never experienced orgasm, or who would like to experience

---

* I use several cassettes such as this. All take a question-and-answer, or conversational, form between me and a client. These tapes are not actual case transcriptions, but dramatic recreations presenting a perfectly typical composite. It should be noticed that each conversation includes many specific suggestions, any one of which may be useful in dispersing the problem.

orgasm more often, self-stimulation is the most direct pathway permitting its achievement. Once a person has learned what feels positive and what her successful arousal patterns are, she can teach her partner.

Learning self-stimulation can be just like learning a second language. It is necessary to practice. Proficiency does not come with the first attempts. As you learn this new skill you may have questions which are not answered on this tape. In this case, please ask your doctor for additional suggestions. Because this may be embarrassing for some women who have not yet learned to speak frankly with their doctors, I have asked a woman who is learning self-stimulation techniques to assist me. I am sure you can learn to talk just as easily with your doctor as Mrs. Baker and I have learned to talk together.

Mrs. Baker, in learning self-stimulation, what was your main concern?

MRS. B.: Well, I guess a major barrier initially was my attitude about self-stimulation or masturbation. As a little girl my mother said it was wrong to touch myself—I felt like it was unnatural. Although I recently read about doing it, I was afraid I might get hooked on masturbation as a style and not be able to respond to my partner.

DR.: As you know by now, these are common concerns. There are probably more myths associated with masturbation than with other forms of sexual behavior. This is why many in the helping professions prefer to use the expression "self-stimulation." Masturbation has been blamed for causing pimples, stunting growth, producing warts, and causing frigidity, to name just a few. None of this is true. Actually, it is a very common behavior for both males and females, whether they are single or married.

The thing to remember is that as you learn more about your own sexual response pattern through self-stimulation, you can become more comfortable with your body and more comfortable about sharing pleasure with your partner.

In practicing self-stimulation, what did you find to be important?

MRS. B.:   I noticed that one of the most important things is to find a comfortable setting, a place where you can have privacy, where you know you won't be disturbed. It's important, too, to make sure that you're not tired and that you have plenty of time. I find the bathroom or the bedroom are the most enjoyable places for me. I must admit, though, I had some hesitation at first—I felt awkward, but I guess this is true of a lot of new things we want to learn.

DR.:   Let's review some of the techniques which others have found to be positive. Mrs. Baker, many women choose to begin by massaging their bodies with a favorite body lotion or oil . . . just enjoying the touch of their skin. It often helps to close your eyes and imagine a special person or place from your past history, a romantic movie setting, a book, or anything else that might be arousing to you.

MRS. B.: It's funny, I knew that many men looked at erotic pictures, but I didn't know that women did things like that too.

DR.: Yes, many women find erotic materials and fantasy very stimulating. The important thing is to relax, think about what makes you feel aroused.

Once you are relaxed, you may want to begin to explore your body to find out what different sensations are produced by a variety of movements of the fingers and hands. As you begin stroking, caress your genital area, see what feels most positive. Experiment and notice how the intensity of the feelings begins to change.

Some women feel uncomfortable using their hands. Some prefer to use the water from the faucet in the bathtub or shower. They position their bodies in such a way their genitals are directly beneath the water stream. A person could use feathers, textured material, clothing, virtually anything you find arousing. Vibrators are another alternative. They can be purchased at department and drug stores. Should you wish some assistance, ask your doctor. Some women find that the sensation of vibration heightens arousal and facilitates orgasm.

No matter how you achieve arousal, be aware of what feels good. Most women find that the clitoral area, the area where the small vaginal lips meet above the vaginal opening, is the most sensitive. As you explore your clitoris, vaginal lips, and the surrounding areas, see what feels most pleasurable to you. Experiment with different touch, rhythm, pressure, and strokes. Notice what increases your sensitivity. Fantasize. Imagine that your partner is with you in the way you like most.

As you learn self-stimulation skills you may begin to notice a feeling of warmth, flushing, perspiration, and vaginal lubrication. These are all signs of increasing sexual excitement.

MRS. B.: You know, I've experienced all those things. But sometimes I feel like I've been climbing a mountain and I'm almost to the top, but I'm just not able to get over to the other side. Do you know what I mean?

DR.: Yes, what you are describing has been described by a lot of women. When a person feels like that, she may be concentrating too much on attaining orgasm rather than just enjoying fully her excitement. It is important to become involved with the process as a participant, rather than attempting to be observer as well. Don't concentrate on orgasm. Instead, focus on what is happening . . . what feels good and arousing. When you discover what that is, enjoy it, and find out how you can enhance that experience. Sometimes simply moving your hands to another part of your body might ease the tension you feel. As you relax, begin stimulating yourself again, concentrating on the pleasuring—not on the orgasm. Remember, no one becomes skillful with a new language on the first attempt. There is always another occasion.

MRS. B.: You know, before I first experienced orgasm, I would worry about losing control. I really didn't know how to act.

Dr.:   When someone feels that way, we suggest that
            you act out whatever you feel an orgasm will
            be like—before it happens. Make the sounds
            and gestures that you feel might occur if you
            experienced an orgasm. Some women do this
            in front of a mirror. Role playing can help
            eliminate concerns about losing control.

Mrs. B.:   Some friends have told me that some orgasms
            are just super, but others are not. What do
            you think about that, doctor?

Dr.:   Orgasms differ in intensity from occasion to
            occasion and from person to person. The more
            orgasms a person does experience, the more
            intensely they can experience them. The im-
            portant thing is to experiment and discover
            the number of ways you can achieve orgasm.
            If you stimulate yourself and don't have an
            orgasm on that occasion, that's okay. If you
            find that it is becoming work and not pleasure
            —STOP—that's NOT okay—and begin again
            another time.

Mrs. B.:   You know, every time I get excited, I begin
            to think, "Am I going to have an orgasm this
            time?"

Dr.:   Yep, that's common too, Mrs. Baker. If it
            makes you anxious, it may prevent you from
            attaining orgasm. Direct your attention back
            to your body, and as you reach the point of
            orgasm, fantasize about your partner. As you
            learn this new skill you will find your special
            pattern of stimulation. You know, women may
            believe that men magically know all about
            what gives women pleasure. Yet each woman
            is unique, and it is her responsibility to de-

termine her own unique responses and teach those to her partner. Many women have found this to be a beginning step to achieving sexual satisfaction with their partners.

(*If the techniques I have suggested to Mrs. Baker do not work for you, do not hesitate to ask your doctor for other specific suggestions. Elise followed some of these specific suggestions and she experienced orgasm during her fourth practice session, and then she included her husband. Elise and Paul no longer find sex boring. Nor does she find him boring anymore. After 20 years of marriage, Elise finally turned herself on.*)

JACK

Jack was 31, an editor of three trade journals serving the construction industry, had been married seven years, had seen a psychologist with his wife, Barbara, and had been to Esalen twice. He started his tape with the words, "I find that most of the time I have no desire to have sex with my wife. We're down to about once a month." Here, again, let's notice what is in the way of their experiencing sexual pleasure—and then let's have them walk around the barriers, if they wish to!—or have them choose whatever options may be open to them.

"I had my first orgasm at age seven, while doing a chin-up. It felt good, but I had no idea what it was. Then I found other ways to get an orgasm, by rubbing my penis against a table or some other object. (*Asset: The body works and he's imaginative, or once was.*) My aunt caught me once, and when I told her it felt good, she told me to stop or my penis would fall off. I stopped. My aunt scared me. Then I had a wet dream when I was thirteen or fourteen and I felt so ashamed. It was like wetting the bed. Some time later I heard my father talk about the prostate. I asked what it was and he gave me a book that explained the physiology and anatomy of sex. I learned what masturbation was and I started doing it. (*Asset: He found out it was okay.*) But I kept everything a secret. I felt ashamed of masturbating. If I'd ever been caught, I'd have felt even greater shame. (*Was it really okay?*) I always did it alone. I didn't date in high school, and the only sexual relationships in college were when I went to a whorehouse with friends. I had a bad experience there—I couldn't get an erection and the girl said I masturbated too much. (*He probably wondered how she knew that. She probably said that to anyone who didn't get it up. That's called playing it safe; most boys think they masturbate too much.*)

"I found that I enjoyed masturbating so much that I still do it. It's an easier experience for me than having sex with somebody else. (*Skinner is right. We learn by consequences—in this case, that masturbation works and intercourse does not.*) I know exactly what feels good to me whenever I feel like doing it, and I don't have to worry about making somebody else feel good. I can just masturbate for the pure orgasm, and I feel more comfortable masturbating than I do having sex with my wife. (*He's being selfish and not at all otherish; they're really made of the same substance—giving/getting.*)

"At the same time, I still feel ashamed of masturbating. (*Of course, he learned well.*) I try very hard to masturbate as little as possible and I feel I am being unfair to my wife by doing it. (*He could stop doing it alone.*) I feel that I've only got so many sexual experiences (*Myth: Just so much lead in the pencil*), and if I masturbate, then I won't feel like having sex with my wife. (*He's set himself up to fail—feeling guilty—by believing the myth, the lead-in-the-pencil theory. He's stuck in the numbers game, scarcity.*

He could play another game called "abundance" instead. That's where you never run out of lead or pleasure. You just need to learn how to recycle it.)

"It hasn't worked out that way. I can go two, three weeks without masturbating and have sex with my wife. And then if I do masturbate, it doesn't really seem to affect the frequency of having sex with Barbara. Whether I masturbate once a week or once a month, I still have intercourse with my wife about once a month. (*The two seem unrelated. They could be related to advantage.*)

"I've recently had sexual fantasies that I don't consider ideal (*What fantasies might he consider ideal?*), but they've turned me on. They involved group sex. I've had fantasies where there's a group and a girl undressed and everybody does everything to her. A man puts his penis in her mouth. A girl has sex with her. People rub her down with oil. She goes into ecstasy. Someone else puts a finger up her anus. I've had fantasies where I'm the one in the middle of a group like that. (*Asset: He seems to be able to fantasize vividly. Liability: He acts as if he has no control over the fantasy's contents. The truth is, he does. He creates them.*)

"I've also had homosexual fantasies. When I was in college I found myself very much attracted to a particular boy I knew. I was aware of the attraction and had some fantasies about having sex with him. I have had fear that I'm abnormal because of the sexual attraction I've felt for some men and the fantasizing I did about men while I was masturbating. (*He's bought another macho myth, not realizing this behavior is common, and okay. He worries that he's a latent homosexual; maybe I'm a latent millionaire—I don't know what "latent" really means.*) I always fantasized about having sexual relations with women during the same period. (*What would he like to think about when he masturbates? Will the thoughts serve him well?*)

"One of the problems my wife and I have had is, many times when we've had sex, I've been ready and when I attempted to enter my wife, she was not ready. It was hard to get my penis in, and many times it was a painful experience. I found I wasn't looking forward to sex. (*He sounds like Elise.*) I didn't want to go through with the whole thing of trying to get my wife ready and then putting my penis in and finding she was closed and I had to either force it in gradually or take it out and engage in foreplay so she'd be ready. Then, while we were engaged in foreplay, I'd feel I wasn't adequate because she wasn't ready when I was. I would often lose my erection, and the sex would never come off. (*Great examples of classical and operant learning—learning by association and consequence—not among rats and pigeons, but among us marvelous people.*)

"I went with a girl when I was twenty-two, my first real serious long-term relationship, although there wasn't any intercourse. There was heavy petting. We would lie naked in bed and do everything we could think of short of intercourse. (*Asset: They were imaginative.*) I had oral-genital relations with my wife. She enjoyed fellatio, but not cunnilingus—she said it tickled, she said she was too sensitive for that. Recently we've not been doing fellatio either. (*Liability: They've stopped doing something that worked. They've turned a "did" into a "don't."*)

"We both began smoking marijuana early in the relationship and found it enhanced our sex, it removed inhibitions. We've had our best experiences when we were both high on marijuana. I don't know why, somewhere along the way we both stopped using marijuana.

"We went to a weekend seminar in sex at someone's house a few months ago, where they urged couples to try hand manipulation, urged greater communication about what did and didn't feel good. I did it once with Barbara and she tried it twice on me. It felt good the second time.

For some reason we haven't done it again. (*He ignores the "dids"—what worked—over and over again. He could do the "dids" again.*)

"Right now my feeling about sex is somewhat discouraged. I feel that it's going to be very difficult for us to work it out, and sometimes I get the feeling that I'd like to have a sexless relationship and forget about sex. (*Liability: He's setting it up for failure. He could think that it's going to be very easy.*) I think that if maybe I masturbate once in a while, and not have to be bothered working so hard, it'd be best. If it doesn't come naturally, then the hell with it. (*He sounds like Elise again.*) But before it gets to that point, I'd like to try to work it out. I guess I figure if I don't try, our marriage will probably not last, and I'd like to keep it going." (*Purposefullness: He hasn't given up, no matter how negative he sometimes sounds. If they wish to learn to enjoy sex with each other, they could. For a starter, he could show her how he did chin-ups and table rubs. In order to facilitate this openness, I gave him an audio cassette reproduced below: "Teaching your partner about you." Mr. Bromley, the composite client in the tape, is clearly a sexual winner.*)

DR.:   Hello, I'm Dr. Ron Pion and I would like to offer some suggestions which I believe may enhance your sexual satisfaction and specifically may assist you in teaching your partner about you. Once a person has learned what feels positive and what his successful arousal patterns are, he can learn to communicate this knowledge to his partner.

Something important to remember is that it takes time to learn all new skills, so don't expect immediate results; do take time to enjoy teaching your partner. Should you wish additional suggestions, or if you have questions which are not answered on this tape, don't hesitate to ask your doctor. Because some people are hesitant to speak frankly about such subjects, I've asked a gentleman to talk with me today, so that you can see how easy it really can be.

Mr. Bromley, how did you feel about communicating with your partner about sex?

MR. B.: Well, initially rather awkward. You see, I've grown up believing that men are naturally supposed to know what's sexually pleasing to them and to their partners. I've also believed that sharing information with my wife about what pleases me is not spontaneous and not natural, and that for her to discuss her desires with me was aggressive, unladylike behavior. I've recently learned that everyone—men and women—differ in their sexual arousal patterns, so it's of great importance for me to let my wife know what I find most arousing . . . for me to communicate my desires, my likes, my dislikes to her. Stating my preferences, actually both of us sharing our preferences, isn't unnatural or unspontaneous; it's an opportunity to share and to expand our relationship.

DR.: You've learned as a matter of fact, if you don't state your preferences, both of you can lose. For example, if you're sitting at dinner and you wish some butter, you simply say, "Pass the butter, please." You don't worry "Does she like me if she's not passing the butter?" or "Can't she see that I need the butter?" You simply say, "Pass the butter, please." The very same thing can be true for the expression of sexual wishes and desires.

I seem to remember that you were concerned about your wife only being interested in intercourse in that one position which you called the missionary position.

MR. B.: Yes, that's the way it was. For almost our entire marriage, "sex" consisted of several very routine caresses, followed by intercourse with me on top. Actually, I found our sex life to be kind of dull and uninteresting. I never told her that, except occasionally suggesting that we might try another position or another technique. I guess I was too embarrassed to let her know that I didn't find our sexual routine very stimulating.

DR.: And yet, your sexual activity together needn't be looked at as a routine, or even limited to one set of behaviors, does it?

MR. B.: Exactly, I found that what's most important for increasing my desire and arousal is relaxing and enjoying another's body. We learned to suggest pleasing one another at different times. We let one night be my night and allowed my wife to please me. The next night became her night and I pleased her. We learned to take showers together and to give each other massages with our favorite lotions and oils. Throughout, we discussed what felt good and exciting for both of us . . . where I wanted to be touched and how hard and how soft. At first we stayed away from the genital areas and learned to explore the rest of our bodies. I actually discovered certain areas of my feet that I never knew could be sensuous. During other sessions we included the genitals. We avoided intercourse for the first few pleasuring sessions, but if orgasm did occur it was okay. The primary purpose of these sessions is the exchange of information with one another about what arouses each of us. It really became all right for me to share information about my likes and dislikes with my wife, and for me to learn about her desires.

DR.: Do you remember how you began to experiment with new positions for sexual pleasure during intercourse?

MR. B.: I found out during one of the pleasuring sessions, while my wife was giving me a massage, that I really enjoyed being stimulated while lying on my back. We then sort of agreed to have intercourse with her on top. We soon learned to vary the positions of our legs and arms so that we could continue to arouse one another. It was during one of these times that we discovered how much I enjoyed having my wife caress my thighs and my testicles. Actually, my wife learned to experience more desire, and occasionally we continue to engage in sexual activity after I've reached an orgasm. During these occasions I didn't always have a full erection.

DR.: Did that pose any particular problem?

MR. B.: Well, actually it took us a long time to learn that an erect penis is certainly not necessary for either of us to experience sexual satisfaction.

DR.:   But what if she's aroused, and you don't have an erect penis?

MR. B.:   Well, if you're not in the mood for intercourse, there are other ways you can satisfy your partner . . . like through manual or oral stimulation. Any way two people enjoy sex is okay. Some people find it helpful to pay special attention to the setting. You can enhance the mood by arranging an evening for two out at a restaurant, using music or candlelight at home, perfume, a special outfit, or anything that either of you find arousing.

DR.:   Excellent, Mr. Bromley.

MR. B.:   You know I feel more and more comfortable about asserting myself sexually . . . and my partner has been pleased by my ability to communicate about sex.

(Jack's wife Barbara was not interested in having the marriage work and chose to end the relationship, leaving him for another. Jack also has found a new partner, and both are winners today.)

BUFFY

Remember Buffy, who thought sex was really yucchy? She was the 27-year-old wife of a policeman and the mother of two children, aged two and three.

"The problem I feel I have is I really dislike sex. I feel if I have to satisfy my sexual desires I would rather masturbate (*she sounds like Jack*) and hide in a closet by myself and not let anyone see me or know, rather than to get into bed and have sexual pleasure with my husband. I dislike seeing my husband's naked body. (*Notice she said "pleasure." And—does she wish to make love dressed, or in the dark?*) I dislike it very much. I don't like touching his genital area at all—it really bothers me. I get lumps in my throat. I feel very uncomfortable. I feel pressure and very tense inside. (*She could learn to use feathers rather than fingers. He might like it, and that way she wouldn't actually have to touch.*) When we have sexual intercourse and foreplay beforehand, I just don't get aroused. My mind's wandering. I'm wondering if the neighbors are hearing me, or if the kids are going to wake up. (*She's not participating. She could call the neighbors and ask if they hear anything. She could notice how often the children actually wake up and walk in. She could lock her bedroom door.*) I guess I'm wondering in my subconscious mind if my mother is looking down. (*Buffy, are you suggesting that your mother is a voyeur?*) When we do have sex, I have a problem of getting off him or getting him off me and going to clean myself up. The sperm that gets on my legs and everything just really gets me upset. (*He could wear a condom.*) It makes me want to throw up. I just think it's disgusting. (*What would she like it to be like? What could she do about it?*)

"I even make excuses so that I don't have to go to bed with my husband. I will not let him touch me (*Where?*) during my menstruation period. I feel that's a yuccchy time. (*For what? How about everything short of penetration? Is it a yuccchy time for that, too?*) I feel very unclean and dirty and very cheap. I guess just everything about sex I dislike. There's something wrong that my husband cannot by his own touch just get me aroused. (*Has she taught him yet? She could take him into the dark closet with her next time.*) I don't get aroused by a kiss very easily, if at all. Sexual words (*which ones?*) while playing around in the bedroom or while having intercourse completely repulse me, stop me cold. (*She could learn words to "start her warm."*) I just don't like to try anything new. Just the whole husband-wife relationship of intimacy in the bedroom or wherever, him touching my body, my breasts, really bothers me. I will not touch anything of his. I am very uncomfortable about sex. (*How much longer do you intend to remain uncomfortable, Buffy?*) Almost every day I'm wondering in my mind if I'm going to have to go through it again that night.

"As far as what I've done about the problem, absolutely nothing, besides forget it. I think it's gotten worse. I'm afraid of what's going tò happen to me. I don't know— I'm afraid of what kind of a person I'm going to be. (*What kind of person would she like to be?*) Is sex going to be really free, or am I going to seek out and find someone else? It's very frightening. I feel almost like a child. I want to curl up like a ball and go cry in a corner. (*How much longer do you intend . . . ? Perhaps it's time to do something else, to think something else, to feel something else. How? Learn and then practice.*)

"I wish my husband wasn't such an Almighty God type of a person. (*And all this time I thought it was sex she didn't like.*) This is what he relays to me, and when I get in bed with him I can still feel it. I wish the tension that I have when I am with him would go away. I feel very on guard. I'm afraid to speak.

"In the hopes that I won't be nearly as skeptical or afraid to try some of the sexual freedoms and desires, I bought *The Joy of Sex*, and when I opened the book I got sick to my stomach looking at the pictures, seeing the naked bodies. Which is silly, when I think that I've got two children. (*She notices her inconsistency.*)

"As far as where I learned about sex, my mother and father to this day won't even say the word 'sex'—they spell it. I remember when I was a little girl, the first time I masturbated, my mother caught me. That night I got the worst licking of my life from both of my parents, mostly from my mother. And really degrading me with words, saying what a bad girl I was for masturbating, telling me if I masturbated anymore I wasn't going to have children and people would think I was a bad girl. Then the next day she got me in the car and drove me to the doctor's office. I can vividly see his office. He sat me on top of his table and told me, 'Young lady, you're a very bad, naughty girl!'

"I remember when I started my period for the very first time, my older half-sister broadcast it all over . . ."

(*And on and on Buffy's history went. You've already read much of it in the chapter about learning. Her first experience in bed, with her husband-to-be, was painful. She got pregnant and the priest called her a whore. She was forbidden to wear white or be married in a church. Her mother banished her from visiting her hometown during the pregnancy, said it drove her to a nervous breakdown. It was clear that Buffy had learned that sex was yuccchy.*)

"I remember all of the bad things related to sex very vividly, and there are very, very few times where there are happy times related to sexual relationships. (*Asset: But there are some. What were they? What are they? What could they be?*)

"I think my children might have a big part in my hang-up. I feel so very much a mother I don't have time to play like a child with my husband the way I want it to be. It's kind of hard playing with a man who comes home from work, takes off his clothes, gets into some grubs, and sits in front of the goddamned boob tube, watches it all night. There's just no communication. I believe this to be a big problem. And I think the communication problem stems from I'm afraid to talk to him. (*This is the second time she's mentioned being "afraid." Maybe she just doesn't like the man she's married to.*) He always has this facade of the high and mighty, that he can do no wrong, or else he can twist things around so he doesn't lose, but I lose. And I don't like losing. (*No one does.*)

"I want to be loved. I don't feel as if I am loved in the
fullest way. Little gifts brought home to me, little things,
knowing that I know he's thinking of me, that means so
damned much. Up until this year, which has been almost
six years, I've never received a birthday present, a Christmas present, Mother's Day present—never! I have sent
flowers, bringing him cards for no reason, buying him
presents for 'happy this' and 'happy that,' just to let him
know I'm thinking about him. And I never seem to get
anything in return.

"Sometimes I read between the lines and wonder what
he's really saying. He's such an exact person, and everything has to be in perfectionist order. But I really get
bugged. I want him to trust me and not to always down-
grade me, not to put a price tag on my head, saying you
better enjoy this because it cost me a lot of money. That
really hurts. I want to be put on an equal basis. (*Purposefullness: She's full of it.*)

"I feel very inferior to him. I feel that he covers up his
problems and dumps them on me. This problem I feel is
both of our problem, but it's dumped on me. He might say
it's not, but everything he says makes it be dumped on
me. He has little words that come out of his mouth that
make it stick right onto me as if to say, 'Hey, you're the
cause of this.' Just little words. (*Like what? More im-
portantly, what does she want him to say instead?*) It
makes me very uncomfortable. He's always the one to
speak up first and to answer the proper way, and I'm always hemming and hawing and pulling into my shell and
feeling again that I want to get into that embryo and have
somebody to guide me, because I can't run my own life."

*No matter how negative (demoralized) this sounds,
Buffy came through with an "A" in fantasy. You've seen
part of it before in the last chapter, as an example of a
good, productive fantasy.*

"It is evening time and I am with my husband. Maybe we're just lying together on the deck of a ship, or sitting together on the sand, or running down the beach. Things like that mean a lot to me. Just tender touching. (*Where?*) Not a mind wandering on what's happening in business. Just tender touching. Tender caressing. (*Where?*) I feel sex is a tender thing, I want it to be the gentlest of things possible. And how it ends is the two of us are just lying side by side, loving each other and relaxing. He could be rubbing my back, or we could be walking hand in hand down the beach, very, very close and kicking up the sand with each other.

"I don't really fantasize well, because I never fantasized about sex before. (*Sounded okay to me. What have you fantasized about?*) I see a lot of things in movies and I say, 'Hey, wow, wouldn't that be neat?' (*Wouldn't what be neat? It's possible to make "that" real.*) And then I say, 'Don't kid yourself—that's not the way it really is.' " (*Yet.*)

(*This is a terrific tape. Buffy's asking for equality. Her statement is a declaration. She could have made such a tape as this for her husband, to let him know how she felt and thought. Because communication seemed to be of primary importance, I suggested she listen to another version of the "Teaching your partner about you" tape. This message is very much like the one given to Jack. Only a couple of paragraphs, and of course the voices, differ. As before, the client is a winner:*)

DR.:   Mrs. Green, how did you feel about communicating with your partner about sex?

MRS. G.:   I don't know why, but at first I thought it would be difficult. You see, I believe that men are supposed to know what to do and that women aren't supposed to be aggressive. However, I learned every woman differs in her sexual arousal patterns, so it's important for her to let her partner know what she finds most arousing—to communicate her desires. Stating a preference isn't being aggressive. It's being assertive.

DR.: Do you remember how you got over your frustration about not having orgasm during intercourse? Perhaps you would like to share some of those ideas.

MRS. G.: Some people find that putting the penis in the vagina without thrusting and continuing stimulation of the clitoris is extremely arousing. If that's so for you, continue increasing arousal either through manual stimulation or by use of a vibrator. At the point of your orgasm, if you wish, your partner can begin pelvis movement. With each practice session, he can begin entering the vagina and thrusting earlier. Experimentation with different positions frees up your hands for greater stimulation. You might try being on top, which allows both of you direct stimulation of the clitoris. Experiment with a variety of positions and find out what suits the two of you best. You don't have to be equally aroused, nor do you need to have simultaneous orgasms to enjoy your sex life. The more you practice, the more likely you are to experience an orgasm with his penis in your vagina.

(Buffy noticed she masturbated to orgasm easily in the closet, and in time "came out of the closet" and learned to enjoy sex. She also learned that her husband was un-

willing to change his rough-and-tumble lovemaking ways to accommodate her desire for "tender touching" and in time she left him, to go on to experience joy, satisfaction, and exhilaration in sex with a new marital partner.)

CHAPTER

11

"I Want It More Often (Than My Partner Does)"

This is more commonly, but not always, a man's complaint, and when I hear it I always get the feeling that the person with the complaint believes that he or she is right and that his or her partner is wrong (perhaps sick). Usually these people are, really, asking me to "fix" their partners. It would be easier if they asked me to let them change. After all, most people who eat more than their spouses don't complain to anyone about that; they just eat more and get on with life.

RICHARD

Richard was 46, a building contractor and active in the politics of his home city (population 40,000). He and Marie had been married 25 years, had five children and one grandchild.

"For most of our marriage I was of the opinion that our

sex life was normal. (*It was.*) It began to dawn on us about five years ago, after I read some books and saw some movies which were generally unavailable before, that the sex life that we were leading wasn't the beginning and end of it all. People were doing it in other ways. (*What he's thinking is, "We weren't doing it right."*)

"The problem has been one that's been rearing its head on a sort of weekly basis for the past couple of years. I've been getting uptight about the fact that I have to make the overtures. It's been a nighttime ritual. The act is initiated in the bedroom and it's been without any great eroticism, and in the recent months it's been over as far as I've been concerned in a matter of minutes. (*Liability: This is a "didn't"—the way it has not worked, yet they continue to do it.*)

"The fact that I love her so much and she arouses me so much is in fact causing me a problem, because there's been many a time I've been so overwhelmed by something she's said or done that I wanted to get it on, even in the middle of an afternoon, and she's told me, 'Don't be silly.' (*Asset: She's desirable, he's arousable.*) So I've done some pretty stupid things lately to try to wear off this sex drive. (*He believes there is such a thing.*) I've taken up sky diving. I took lessons and stayed with it until I hurt my leg and decided I'd give that up. I play a mean game of squash and I wore myself out. There've been times when I've told her I was, to use another phrase, horny, and she's nicely told me it wasn't the time or place, and why didn't I take a cold bath. (*Asset: He'll do nearly anything to accommodate her in the postponement of sex. He may accommodate her in sexual ways as well—ways he merely hasn't thought of yet.*) One can take only so many cold baths. (*And cold shoulders.*) So I masturbated, more often than I've had sexual relations. (*And probably did it with some degree of shame and without productive fantasies.*)

"I learned my basic sex knowledge in my teens from the boys at school because I attended an all-boys' school. I really came into contact with girls the first time when I was about fifteen or sixteen, when I dated the girl who lived next door. Nothing sexually happened between us except that I became very aroused after being with her, went home, took a bath, and masturbated. That was my sex life. (*He learned that particular pattern before meeting his wife.*)

"I met my wife when I was about eighteen, and after a year of going with her, she allowed me to fondle her breasts. Another year, I think, passed before we petted heavily enough for ejaculation to take place. Fear, however, of pregnancy precluded intercourse until we became engaged, when I was twenty and she was nineteen. (*No mention of her orgasms.*) We married shortly after my twenty-first birthday, and still no one discussed sex with us. It was considered that we'd learn it as we went along. I think it must have been the seventh or eighth year of marriage before my wife indicated that she would get some pleasure if I manually touched her clitoris. Oral sex was something I not only never heard of, but certainly never even considered as being something to even try. We only in the last five years experimented with other than what I call the standard positions, that is, man superior or woman superior."

Richard's fantasy was predictably linked to his goal (*his purposefullness*), even though he said fantasy was "rather difficult . . . because this is not a thing I've been into at all."

"I would like to be able to find my wife with the soft music bit and the candlelight. You know, exotic nightdress, revealing, ready to 'attack' me as I walk in. (*How about "enjoy"?*) That's the way I see a fantasy.

"I don't believe that our marriage can continue at its present level with me knowing that while she loves me in a rather platonic way, there is nothing there sexually. I am seeing and possibly overemphasizing to myself the passing of the years and the possible diminishing of my sexual powers. I am saying I don't want this to happen. I want to be sexually stimulated by my wife."

(*Richard was so typical, and so ready. I suggested that he and his wife listen to a tape together. This tape is about "sexual satisfaction" and, unlike the others presented thus far, it takes the form of a monologue rather than a dialogue between the client and therapist.*)

The topic I'd like to discuss with you is one that I'll call sexual satisfaction, or sexual responsiveness. The whole subject of sex is surrounded by discomfort, embarrassment, misinformation, and, unfortunately, a lot of unhappiness. I think that married people, at the very least, should enjoy sexual activity. If you're uncomfortable listening to this tape, I hope the feeling soon passes. If possible, I really would like for you to listen to this tape with your wife.

Since sexual satisfaction means enjoying that which you're doing, it doesn't matter really to anybody other than you and your partner what it is you do. There is nothing wrong with sexual activity, providing the two people concerned have mutual respect and understanding for each other. There are certain aspects of sexual activity that might turn your wife on and you off, and vice versa. You can only find out about these by talking about them. Everyone doesn't have to have orgasm, either at the same moment or right after one another. You know that's one of the many prevailing myths.

Just like the myth that only sexual intercourse leads to normal sexual gratification. Still another myth says people have to have orgasms at the same time. Couples don't have to have orgasm at the same time. Couples should be sexually satisfied. But on a Thursday evening it might be her occasion because she feels most like it. On a Monday night, it might be geared for your satisfaction because you feel most like it.

You don't have to have an erection in order to gratify your wife, your partner. You don't have to roll over and go to sleep right after you've ejaculated, or come. You are the expert when it comes to teaching your partner how to bring you to the heights of sexual gratification and she is the expert in teaching you how to bring her to the heights of sexual satisfaction. Not marriage manuals. Not my talking to you, but you two together, communicating together, what it is that turns you on as individuals. Only you two are the experts, because only you two know what it is you like and what it is you don't like.

But don't magically think that your wife knows. And your wife can't and shouldn't magically think that you know what it is she likes, unless that's what you talk about.

You see, we've grown up with this nonverbal thing about sex. You don't talk when you have sex. I don't know why people don't talk when they have sex, except they haven't learned to. But how else can people convey likes and dislikes except verbally or except with certain new signals? This doesn't mean you have to talk exactly at the moment when you're involved with sexual activity. You can talk about what happened moments later. You can talk about what will happen in several moments, or in an hour; it really might be your style to moan and groan and sigh and be happy and not talk. That's all right. You

don't have to. You do have to communicate. You do
have to develop signals. And when something happens that you don't like, say you don't like it.

Men and women have for years practiced forms of
self-stimulation and self-satisfaction. Studies long
ago showed—and by the way, made people comfortable when they read the studies and found out
that they weren't unique individuals and really were
like other people—these studies showed that men
masturbate (with a much greater frequency, by the
way, than do women) and women masturbate too.
That word "masturbation" seems to carry with it
some discomforting connotations. Self-stimulation?
Maybe a better phrase. What self-stimulation im-
plies is producing sufficient stimuli to your body to
produce sexual satisfaction, often in the form of an
orgasm.

If two people are together and lovingly caress, touch,
kiss, that is sexual behavior. If a man ejaculates or a
woman has an orgasm at a time when such caressing
is going on, even before a penis has been inserted in a
vagina, that's sexual responsiveness and satisfaction.

It's funny how a lot of marriage manuals, hoping to
increase our particular knowledge and our particular
satisfaction, introduced some funny words or phrases
like foreplay, something you do before you do "it!"
But foreplay is also "it." Any sexual activity or behavior is "it." "It" (sex) is touching and warmth and
affection and stroking and caressing. "It" is everything
that you two people, as people, enjoy.

Oral-genital practices—tranlated into more common
terms, kissing a man's penis or a man kissing a
woman's clitoris—are forms of sexual satisfaction that

many couples have been practicing since the beginning of time. Some women enjoy orgasm when their clitoris is being caressed by their husband's tongue or their husband's finger. Some men enjoy having an orgasm when their penis is being kissed by their partner's mouth or being touched by their partner's hand.

It doesn't matter how you and your partner enjoy each other sexually. It does matter that you do enjoy each other sexually. You can learn from one another. You can grow together. There is a joy of experimentation, and there's nothing wrong when it's based upon mutual respect and understanding. It's important that in the area of sex and satisfaction between man and woman, husband and wife, there are but two experts—the man and the woman. Find out from your partner what pleases her. Discuss it, enjoy it.

Remember, there are people who can help you enjoy sexual activity more. Ask for help. Don't be embarrassed to talk about something that we, as human beings, have been doing for thousands and thousands of years.

(*I suggested that Richard and his wife verbalize their sexual preferences and fantasies while massaging each other. When they protested that they knew nothing about massage, I shrugged and suggested they get some baby oil and let their hands and imagination do the rest. They did. It is nearly impossible to tell anything but the absolute truth when kneading your partner lovingly, and very soon Richard's erections started lasting longer and she began to come on to him. The incidence of activity increased from a basically mechanical, uninterested once a week to sometimes more than once a day. They opened themselves up and got full of purpose and hope and became winners.*)

12

"We Don't Do It Anymore"

. . . and they are too proud to admit their foolishness to one another. They have painted themselves into a corner and rather than get out of the corner—change position—they have opted for pathology instead. They are saying, "There must be something wrong with me, him, her, us."

PATTI AND ANDY

Patti was 26 and a bank teller, living with Andy, a senior in law school. One of six children, she believed that her upbringing, by generally liberal parents, gave her an open attitude about sex. But . . .

"We have a lack of physical responsiveness. In other words, we do not have any sex whatsoever. Our physical responsiveness is just to the point of hugging and kissing and that's as far as it goes. (*Where does she hug him? Where could she hug him?*) We have known each other almost four years and we have had this problem of no sex for the last two and a half or three years.

"I think the problem started when I had gone into the airlines as a stewardess and had left the Islands for a while. We had been separated for about four months, and then I was flying back and forth to Honolulu when we saw each other and had sex frequently. Then, about six months later, I quit the airlines and the airlines quit me. I preferred to be here with my partner all the time instead of four or five times a month. So I was upset about leaving the airlines, but I was glad about being with my partner. I came back here and I moved in with him and I was a bit depressed about the entire situation, and I knew I was going to have to look for a job, but wasn't enthusiastic about looking immediately, so I just more or less threw my burden upon his shoulders, hoping that he would help me out of my depression. However, it seemed to backfire. I guess I was relying on him too much. He didn't like that. I think we had sexual relations several times after I had returned, and that probably lasted for a month, and then suddenly he just stopped. (*Sounds like she scared the sex out of him.*)

"I finally got over being depressed about the job problem when I found my present job, but unfortunately I was still left with no sex. I would talk to Andy, and the only response I would get was, 'No,' and when I would ask why, he would say he didn't know. (*That's the truth.*) I'd talk to him again after a month or so, and he'd become more open each time. (*Asset: They talk. Without sexual satisfaction so far, but many, many others don't talk at all.*) He would say he'd try to do something about it, and my spirits would be lifted again. Time would go by and nothing would happen.

"I think I went through periods of thinking: Let's forget

it and not see each other anymore, let's cool the relationship (*doesn't need cooling*) and start dating other people. Only I didn't want to do those things. (*Could have seduced him openly, honestly, lovingly.*) I wanted to stay with him. I went through crying periods, pleading periods, ridiculing him at times. (*You can bet this was a real "didn't." No one responds to this with affection.*) During all this period we were sleeping together frequently without sex. I guess I was convincing myself that this was what it was going to be like and I was going to be content with it. (*Liability: She programmed herself for failure—creating negative self-emptying prophecy, instead of self-fulfilling fantasy.*)

"During this two-and-a-half-year period I never have had any relations with anybody else. I don't think he has. I'm not really sure whether he doesn't want to have sex with me, or he's just not interested in sex at all. I guess if he wanted to have sex, he could very easily dump me and go after someone else on the side. (*I wondered if they were experiencing orgasm by themselves during this time, and what their fantasies were, if indeed they were orgasmic. They were, and they were not self/other-serving.*)

"In some ways our relationship is wonderful. I think Andy has really brought a lot of things out of me. I was very much of an introvert. I didn't talk to people who were even close to me about my family and my past. He drew all of these things out of me and showed me that it really wasn't such a horrible thing to let someone know about your feelings. My father really doted on my brother—the only boy—and so I wanted to be like him and, when my father would tell my brother a boy's not supposed to cry, well, I thought my father probably would like me more if I didn't cry. I learned to repress my tears. Andy showed me it was okay to cry, and he helped me to cry for sadness, cry for joy. (*Asset: She has a self/other relationship with Andy at times that provides rare and delicious intimacy.*)

"But we still didn't have sex, and this is when I started masturbating, probably as an outlet for myself. I needed (*wanted*) some type of satisfaction sexually. (*Could tell him she's doing it, offer to let him watch, ask him to participate.*)

"I can't help remembering the time before we stopped having sexual relations. We were getting to the point where we were experimenting—having sex in different ways. By that I mean different positions. (*Did work before, could work again.*)

"I love my partner very much. He's good to me. We don't fight. By fighting, I mean yelling at each other. If we have a disagreement, we can sit down and talk about it, tell each other our views. (*There's the communication asset again.*) But I think our sexual problem has gone too far and I'm limited as to what to talk about because of my lack of sexual experiences. I think I've gone through all my ideas." (*Readiness: She knows there are more ideas around somewhere. I am about to let them "get well." How easy it will be. They only think something is wrong!*)

Patti's fantasy naturally involved her partner. The setting was the ever popular "white sandy beach on a warm and sunny day." I've always lived, and practiced, within a few miles of the beach. I wonder what they daydream about in St. Louis?

"It's probably about high noon and we have just had our picnic, eaten our lunch and we're in the water. He decides he wants to have sexual intercourse. He proceeds to take off my bathing suit, wrap it around his neck, take off his bathing suit. We swim around in the nude for awhile. We play with each other. We touch each other. I love touching a male's nude body, my partner's nude body. Then all of a sudden he sweeps me out of the water and runs me up on the sand and lays me down on the blanket, and he proceeds to screw me. Then we go back into the water nude and swim around, and get back out of the water and lie on the beach nude for a while. Andy and I stay there until sunset and have sex while the sun is going down. I think that's a good way to end the day . . . and probably a good way to start the day too."

Andy was an only child of what he described as "ultra-ultra-conservatives," Canadians who emigrated to the U.S. when he was four or five. Upon graduation from law school, he intended to join a local firm specializing in real estate.

"When Patti and I met, we really seemed to hit it off well. When sex came into the picture it was really great. (*Did work, could work again.*) Approximately three months after we started dating she got a job as a stewardess, something she always wanted. And I was very proud of her.

"At that time she went into training on the mainland, and I would see her on occasions when she'd come in for a turn-around for two or three hours, occasionally for weekend trips. Our sex seemed to be greater during that time. (*And he could work hard when she left.*)

"About three months after Patti became a stewardess she was relieved of her duties. Apparently she was fired from her job. This was a great disappointment to her, and it was to me also, because it was something she always wanted to do and I was proud of her at that time. In order to punish her for this, my whole feelings about her sort of changed, in that I shut her off from sex. (*Didn't know what else to do! But it was a pretty stupid thing for a smart fellow like him to do.*) I've always been a very hard worker as far as occupation goes. In coming over here about five years ago, I started from scratch, working very hard, at the same time going back to college and then to law school, still working on the side to afford the tuition.

When Patti was relieved of her duties at the airlines, the whole world sort of fell out from under her. She was really down in the dumps, and it took her quite a while to get on her feet and start looking for a job. I always talked to her and asked, 'Did you go out and find something?' 'No.' 'Why not?' 'Well, I didn't feel like it.'

"This went on for months and months. She'd stay in the house. At times I heard comments like, 'Well, I don't really have to go to work because you'll take care of me.' (*And he was thinking: Like hell I will—I'll show her.*) This was totally against my principles of very hard work. So this would prolong and encourage and build up this sexual barrier, and I'd keep shutting her off."

Still, his fantasy matched Patti's perfectly. All that really differed was the location.

"I'd be right here in the bedroom of my apartment. The time? In the evening, possibly seven, eight o'clock at night. It's raining out. The person I'm with—I would like it to be Patti. What's happening? I've just finished taking a swim in the apartment house pool, I'm taking a shower and then I'm relaxing, lying down. There's a cool breeze and a little music in the background. Maybe a back rub, soothing my muscles. Sort of drifting off, and we'd start petting each other, leading to intercourse, with both of us climaxing at the same time, hopefully. Drifting apart, and both of us are taking a little nap after that."

(*This couple's position was so typical of this complaint. They both believed that "there must be something wrong or else we would still be doing it." In fact, there was nothing wrong except that they weren't doing it. All they needed was knowing this, and "permission" to resume having sex. I suggested they start right away, and to make it easy I urged them to tell each other their fantasies. I mean, they already were in each other's fantasies. Why not make the fantasies real? They did, and canceled their next appointment.*)

Others with this complaint, who don't do "it" anymore, may be in a state of near-terminal boredom. Something that often works for these couples—*and* for individuals who want more than their partners do—involves the purchase of two more books, "his and her" copies of Alex Comfort's *The Joy of Sex.*

I suggest that the man and woman go through their own copies, marking a plus (+) or minus (−) in the margins next to the activities or behaviors described, according to whether they approve or disapprove—and then exchange books, thereby discovering (privately and truthfully) new areas of experimentation and potential sexual delight.

CHAPTER

13

"I Can't Get It Up"

"When can't you get it up?" That's my first question. Can you experience erection during self-stimulation? Do you have wet dreams? How about what are called "bladder erections," the erections experienced in the morning on awakening? If the male does not—*ever!*—experience hardness during any of these three occasions, he should seek medical assistance. However, if erection *does* occur in any of these circumstances, he is "normal" and may wish to notice that he has learned to be (think/feel/do) exactly the way he is.

CARLOS

Carlos was 50, production manager of a small San Francisco Bay area plastics company, an avid weekend fisher-

man. *He had been married for five years during his thir-*
ties and was now single.

"I first became aware of this impotence problem following a relationship I had with a girl I met after my marriage
ended. We had a fairly intense relationship, including
sexual activity, and we were considering marriage, at
least in a vague sort of way. Somehow nothing really came
of this, and the girl took a job in another part of the
state and moved away. I was still very fond of her and
several times a year I would find myself near where she
lived, and I found myself trying to rekindle the past
relationship. She felt the same way, but was reluctant to
go to bed with me without some further assurances of
marriage, perhaps. Anyway, it seemed that we had a
pattern of where I would end up spending the night in
her bedroom expending a lot of energy attempting to
have intercourse, with her trying to forestall the whole
thing. And then on one of the trips she sort of finally
came around and was willing; I found that even though
I had what I presumably wanted, I suddenly wasn't able
to do anything about it. (*He learned to turn off—just like*
Elise, Natasha, Mary Jo, etc.) The more I would try, the
more it would be blocked out. I came back on later trips
with the same results. Sometime later I met another girl
and was a little bit apprehensive about a relationship, but
somehow stumbled into one and by and large had no
difficulty in this regard at all. (*Did work, could work*
again.) I wound up being involved with this girl about
three years, seeing her essentially every weekend. And
while there were very occasional times at which I couldn't
perform, this was a rare enough event that neither of us
really considered it a problem. (*Even Babe Ruth struck*
out sometimes.)

"In 1967 this relationship broke up, partially due to
inertia and partly due to the fact that I moved away to
where it was truly inconvenient for us to see each other

very frequently. I had several affairs, very transient ones, following this, most of which rated from barely satisfactory to often a kind of total failure. (*Liability: He's playing the numbers game.*)

"I found myself becoming less aggressive in trying to meet women, but in spite of myself wound up with several relationships, two of which were abortive one-night situations where I wasn't able to perform and essentially either ended the relationship or made no further efforts along a sexual line at all.

"Strangely, during this period the woman I saw for three years came out on vacation and spent several weeks with me, and the old relationship resumed rather normally and easily. (*He could notice that.*) A rather obvious pattern seems to persist that, where I'm really comfortable in a situation, it seems a relationship can be established. (*He seems to need intimacy, which is okay with me.*) Where I'm insecure and it's extremely transient, that's where the problem begins. (*Recreation with another doesn't seem to work.*) Also, it seems as though the problem has intensified over time. It would seem that today my probability of failure in that kind of relationship is extremely high, where in the earlier years it would be considerably less. (*Asset: He knows what "kind" of girl to avoid. Unfortunately, he's been putting himself down for years for being a nice, highly moral man, who deserves to be rewarded for being that. In fact, he is about to be rewarded.*)

"The reason all of this is of particular concern to me now is that I'm planning to get married. I have been divorced about thirteen years, but a few months back I met a perfectly lovely person and we decided to get married. We did wind up in bed, and the almost predictable failure occurred, at which time I decided that I had to seek professional help if there was some way I could find it. (*He called me and learned I was about to leave town.*

We talked and I let him know he could learn to be sucessful . . .) Since then we've had a number of other occasions in bed. In fact, I guess I have almost essentially moved in. And after the first three or four days we did achieve successful, very successful intercourse. (*Did work, could work again.*) And then we had a series of intermittent successes and failures. Here the pattern seems to be that if I try (*and worry about failing*), I fail, and on the other hand, if I don't try, something may or may not magically happen. (*Trying really doesn't work easily. Try to blush. Try to cry. Try to be happy.*)

"Often it occurs in the morning when I wake up with an erection, and since she is rather easily and quickly aroused, I'm able to consummate our relationship without a great loss of time. (*What a great asset. Imagine if he were married to Barbara, Jack's wife.*) I suspect that if I had to take ten or fifteen minutes to arouse her, I might not be able to sustain the erection (*doesn't have to*), that I would somehow feel I was trying something, and once trying something I would fail. So far, once I've achieved penetration, I haven't seemed to have had any difficulty. But as of this point I still have no confidence at all that I can will an act of love and be successful in doing it. (*He could remove a lot of pressure by learning how else his fiancée easily achieves orgasm.*)

"I'm a typical product of an older generation where the whole subject was taboo. There was no discussion around our house. (*It's starting to sound familiar. Grade schoolers today tell me no one talks to them at home or at school about it.*) It wasn't a happy household, either. My parents were constantly bickering, and there was no real evidence of a warm relationship on their part.

"When I was in the eighth grade, I became aware that my penis apparently was a little smaller than normal. (*Erect or nonerect, Carlos? And who said it was smaller than "normal"? And what's "normal"?*) The reason it sticks

in my mind was we had an eighth grade party and we all
went to some resort and went into a dressing room to
change into our bathing suits. There was some kid I
vaguely remember as a bratty older kid who probably
should've been in high school, who began to tease me. As
I grew older it became of some concern to me. I wondered if this would somehow impair my ability to satisfy
a woman. Somehow I managed to go through the service,
sharing a barracks with dozens of men, without a single
reference again to this sort of thing. So I guess objectively
the difference really isn't that significant, but it's still
something I'm very much aware of. (*Asset: He knows
where he's stuck, in confusing size with sighs.*)

"I guess I had a reasonable amount of curiosity and
drive, and desire to get involved with adolescent girls.
But, either because I was inept, or the particular social
groups that I moved with were rather old-fashioned, I
really wasn't able to have an opportunity for intercourse
until I went into the service at age twenty. (*He could
have known that he didn't have to have intercourse.*) Of
course, obviously the circumstances of the war made this
kind of involvement easier, and from time to time I would
have opportunities for intercourse, and with a pattern of
problems that were probably related to my present problem. One was a tendency toward premature ejaculation.
The other was the apparent physical fact that I could
never seem to have intercourse more than once a night.
(*Not many others do, either, regardless of what they
claim.*)

"Meanwhile, most of my friends were coming back and
bragging about three, four, and five times a night. I knew
I couldn't do that. I knew I could do it at night and the
next morning and again that night, but it was only once
and that was it. (*He can do it, and do it, and do it again—
three times in 24 hours, yet he complains of never being
able to do it more than once a night.*) This, I think, made

the problem of premature ejaculation all the bigger for me. Because I would have this feeling that I have this one opportunity (*so much lead in the pencil, again*) to satisfy this girl, and if I don't I'm just not going to be able to do anything more. So I would worry about that and, of course, the more I would worry about premature ejaculation, well, the more you could almost guarantee that it would happen. (*When you worry about something, you are rehearsing.*)

"One of the suggested questions here is to fantasize what an ideal sexual relationship should be. Certainly, I think that's very easy to say right now. It could be with the girl that I plan to marry. (*Great idea. He's learning to use the prophecy of success, setting himself up to win.*) It could be perhaps anytime, but it would be nice if it were light enough so that I could look at her and appreciate the enjoyment and satisfaction which I would see reflected in her face. (*He's being otherish.*) It would end with, I guess, the heightening of senses on both our parts and mutual satisfaction. (*He's selfish/otherish.*)

"I guess if I can summarize, I guess I do have a very real problem—not as bad as I thought it was a couple of weeks ago, because I demonstrated that I still can have intercourse at least once in a while when the circumstances are right (*Hopefullness: it's been happening more lately; it could be a trend*). I am going to marry this girl in about five weeks, regardless of any improvement or deterioration in the intervening time. And I am terribly concerned that I can get better, to give her the normal sex life that she's entitled to." (*Purposefullness: he knows what he wants and is going for it.*)

(*Of all the sexual acts related to "performance," none is more common than the failure of erection. Like so many others with this problem, Carlos used the word "perform." Who, I asked, was watching? Did he really want ap-*

plause—and whose? Was there some Academy Award given in the category called "best lover"—a "Casanova" perhaps, shaped like a you-know-what? The truth was, if Carlos wanted to "perform" he could, with or without an erection. But inasmuch as he wanted to have an erection, and experienced them reliably in the morning at least, I told him that he could. He realized that he was stuck in cognition, focusing on the failures in his past—the "didn'ts" in his life—and forgetting the many "dids." He realized, when told, that these "didn'ts" would never disappear from his past, and that that didn't really matter, because that was behavior he could ignore, focusing instead on his successes. Intimacy was the key. Carlos said he rarely experienced erection failure when his relationship was sincere, as was clearly the case with his fiancée. He came to see me with her, and she was certain they were loaded with assets, not liabilities. They examined their shared successes, used them as a model to create more by duplicating favorable circumstances, such as relaxation and intimacy and long-standing relationship, and avoiding such obvious pitfalls as worry and "performance." They married and may live happily ever after, or at least until they learn to have a new problem. The old one went away.)

Ways to experience sexual satisfaction without intercourse are generally introduced to a male (or couple) complaining of erection failure. A reading of *The Joy of Sex* is recommended. Often when attention is drawn away from erection failure and centered on something untried before, erection occurs, a welcome and wonderful surprise.

CHAPTER

14

"I Can't Keep It Up"

SALLY AND DON

Sally and Don were both 38 and married for nearly 14 years, with no children. Both grew up in the Midwest, and because Don was an oil drilling engineer, they had traveled much of the world. Sally came to see me first.

"We have had problems with sex ever since we were first married. We've tried to pass it off with all kinds of excuses about how one person didn't feel good, the other person didn't feel good. But it just slowly creeps up. I really do not enjoy going to bed with him. I think it's a chore. (*Skinner, take note—you're right. People learn according to how rewarding or punishing the experience. Sally experienced no reward, so she had no fun.*) There are some times when I do enjoy it, but this last year most of the time it seems to be a chore.

"My husband and I have not sought professional help. It was my idea to come in for treatment. I had a hysterectomy about six weeks ago, and we hadn't had any sex up until last week and he had trouble with intercourse our first time. He was able to get it up and then it died; and then continuing on for about three times, and then I decided I just couldn't handle the problem alone. We both want our marriage to work and would like to get our sexual problems organized. Otherwise, our marriage is absolutely perfect. (*Whatever that really means. It makes me nervous if I'm asked to bet on their staying together. You see, people who have absolutely perfect marriages often fail to notice the way it really is.*)

"My first sexual experience was with my husband-to-be. I think it was between the age of seventeen and eighteen. We had neither of us been taught how to protect ourselves against pregnancy. We were just darn lucky. Then I went to college for three years, and when I was twenty-one I joined the airlines and met a man and fell in love, I thought. He would come down for the weekend, and we would have sex together. It was very enjoyable for me, but I didn't have any idea of how to protect myself (*all these years, and she still hasn't thought seriously about birth control*) and I got pregnant. I didn't want to marry him, so I went down to Mexico and got an abortion. After that we broke up.

"After this episode I thought about my relationships with men a lot, finally realizing that I really loved Don. So I called him on the telephone, and we started up our relationship again. We got engaged at Christmastime and were married that June. A week before I walked down the aisle I had a terrible feeling that maybe I was doing the wrong thing. Maybe a lot of girls feel the same way. (*Yup, boys too.*) Now sometimes I look back on it and think maybe I got married on the rebound, and maybe this was the way our relationship was supposed to end.

(*A good way to think if you'd like to end your marriage.*)
It seemed like a good idea, the marriage. My parents were happy. His parents were happy. Everybody was happy. (*How about you, Sally?*)

"About six months ago I started having an affair with a man who's my husband's very close friend, and we go out a great deal. I really feel I love this man. We've had sex about ten times and it's really fantastic. I have orgasms all the time, which I don't have very often with my husband. He's a very easy person to have sex with. He doesn't require any special things. (*Does Don require anything you don't like?*) I feel very relaxed with him. In our discussions with each other, I told him about my abortion. He's the only man I've ever told. My husband doesn't even know about it. I'm sure he would not take it well at all. That's one of the reasons I haven't told him. It's bothered me for many years. (*Liability: I'm always amazed how distrusting people are of those they're married to. And she said this was a "perfect" marriage, remember?*)

"About sexual fantasies. I see a good-looking man and wonder, gee, what would it be like to have him make love to me? I think of the man I'm having an affair with almost all the time. My mind is never blank of him. I think of sex with him all the time, of all the different things we could do together. (*If she wants her marriage to work, she could begin to include the husband in her fantasies.*)

"When we make love, my man friend and I, generally it starts out with a masturbating technique where he uses his fingers and his mouth until I have an orgasm. And then we have intercourse and I have another orgasm. Generally, we have them together. After we have sex, we generally just lie very close to each other and talk about a lot of things, and I just feel very warm, very happy and contented. I never feel guilty about having sex with him. I just feel rejuvenated and happy and gay, and that the whole world is my oyster."

Don followed Sally into my office by three weeks, seeming reluctant to do so, but his tape was among the longest made by a male. (Men's tapes are generally much shorter than women's.) Here are some excerpts:

"The problem for which we are seeking help centers around our apparent mutual dissatisfaction with our sexual relationship. Although I think that both of us have been somewhat disappointed in the past years with one another's performance in the bedroom, the immediate event that precipitated this call for help was my inability to sustain an erection.

"I must remark on my own relative inexperience sexually prior to getting married. Indeed, the woman I married was the only woman with whom I completed a sexual relationship. (*Asset and liability: Could be great instead of a self put-down.*) The reasons for this are not totally clear at this point. However, one of the strong overlying ideas was that one had to be very deeply in love before consummating that love sexually. This is an idea that was implanted in me quite early. (*And it's really an okay idea.*) It's an idea that my parents had and which at an early age I accepted wholeheartedly.

"My parents had a fantastic influence on my sexual thoughts and behavior, and I've come to resent and hate them for it. (*Instead of recognizing their influence and then leaving it alone if it doesn't work now.*) They were extremely conservative in that regard. Sex was for love only, and that produced in me, or with my help I produced in me, enough hang-ups about it that at least on one occasion I walked away from a nude woman in bed when I was in college. I didn't feel like I loved her. Therefore I didn't feel I could make love to her—and I couldn't. I've always resented that. (*He could learn to respect himself for it.*)

"As for my relationship with Sally, honeymoons being what they are, ours was fantastic as well. A lot of new exploring. A lot of new sensations that we both experienced. The honeymoon lasted several years. Still, during this period of time, I developed the idea that I was not able to turn my wife on. More specifically, she was not acting like I expected women who were turned on to act. (*Liability: Counting size instead of sighs.*) This expectation was artificial in retrospect, produced mainly by conversation with 'the boys,' concepts derived from magazines, movies, and very little personal knowledge. (*And no communication with Sally.*)

"Whatever the reason, into our marriage approximately three or four years, I wondered if something was wrong with me if I was not able to stimulate my wife to single orgasm, let alone multiple orgasms, so I had a couple of encounters outside of marriage with girls I had met on my travels. Actually, much to my dismay I found that these women responded to me spontaneously. Our relationships were highly erotic, sexually very satisfying, and a tremendous source of ego food. I expect that this just compounded the problem by now making sexual relationships with my wife appear to be even worse. (*Yup.*)

"I developed an easy out, and that was, there obviously was nothing wrong with me—it had to be her problem.

"The particular woman I'm involved with at the moment, I feel I love dearly. I've known her for a year. We've been through a great deal of her life and my life together as far as sharing experiences together. In fact, it's in many ways sad that I should know and understand the feelings of another woman in many respects better than the woman I've been living with.

"There is a friend of mine who is aware of my current affair and in an indirect way is kind of encouraging it. I am now aware of the fact that this friend—and he remains a friend, although somewhat strained—is the man with whom my wife is having an affair. I know, it really sounds like Monday afternoon TV. (*It is.*)

"Initially this affair was somewhat secret. We'd meet in the most obscure, godawful places. Later we became more open. We went to cocktail bars, occasionally a restaurant. Within recent months, we've even gone places with other people, an idea which other people seem to totally accept. That's been encouraging too.

"Perhaps I should go back to a specific incident. One evening not too long ago my wife and I hopped into the rack in anticipation of wild, passionate love. (*I've never heard a woman describe the act of love as "into the rack." A "rack" is an instrument of torture.*) After initially getting stimulated, I frankly lost interest. There went the erection and up went the anxiety. The next morning I left early for work, got halfway there and decided this was so much bullshit. I was going to turn around and drive home and prove to her and to me that whatever happened the night before clearly wasn't my fault.

"Despite all of her attempts and mine, absolutely nothing happened. Just zero. (*Remember Carlos? You cannot will an act of love.*) And I got up from bed in such an intense rage I couldn't talk. That incident precipitated her calling for help.

"I've thought a great deal about what the ideal sexual relationship is, and I think you have to be in love first. (*Learned from Mom and Dad, after all.*) 'Successful' sex might mean only that you're with a person who meets your physical criteria for the moment and is interesting enough to spend an evening with. But that's not ideal. Ideally you love her. I would. (*Could stop resenting parental teaching.*)

"What's happening in the ideal relationship? Well, that's really what this whole tape is about. I know you don't always have to end up in the saddle (*now he is riding a horse?*) in order to be sexual or to be happy about sex. That's not enough, however, to last forever. In fact, what it does is heighten sexual awareness and has heightened it, so it makes the bedroom scene better when it comes around. Except in my case, when we're in the rack, it just makes me feel more frustrated. (*Could stop going to bed and try the couch, or wherever. Could also stop concentrating so hard on what isn't hard.*)

"Most of the time in my ideal sexual relationship it ends up in bed with some really heavy loving for a while—two, three orgasms—and quietly falling asleep in one another's arms and waking up later. One of the greatest feelings in the world is looking across the pillow one morning or one late afternoon afterward and seeing that great big set of eyes looking at you and telling you, without saying anything, that which you already know."

(These two, among the many people I've met, could have become an ideal couple—only they chose to part. He, in order to be with the person he shared intimacy with. She, for a future relationship that would start differently from this one and continue differently from this one. They're both winning right now.)

A resolution for this problem is identical to that for general erection failure—learning new ways to pleasure each other, and being rewarded with a new erection, too. It is not wise, however, to experience orgasm with a "soft-on," a penis that is partially erect. Rewarding yourself for that is learning how to stay semierect.

CHAPTER

15

"It Hurts"

There is only one response to anyone who says it hurts—STOP! What they are saying is "it hurts . . . *when I do that.*" My response: "Then how come you do that, rather than something else? Pain is not fun, so why continue to experience it? Tell me, what *doesn't* hurt? What feels good? And while you're doing that, tell me what it is you want—specifically?"

NATASHA

Natasha was an assistant principal of an elementary school, married to a young lawyer in the public defender's office. They were both in their early thirties. There were two children.

'When I was growing up as a teen-ager I was a 'good girl.' I didn't fool around. In retrospect, I feel this really hurt me. In complying with the social morals of the time I was really cheating myself out of a lot of valuable experience that would've enhanced my sexual life and my sexual abilities as an adult now. (*Liability: She's playing "if only" to her disadvantage, fails to recognize that it isn't too late to learn.*) There were several cases where I resisted temptation and shut myself down when I could've gone out and enjoyed myself. (*Asset: What power! If she can switch off, she can switch on.*)

"I dated one boy from my sophomore year in high school through my freshman year in college, and because we were teen-agers new to sex, we kind of used each other to explore what sex was all about. We did a lot of necking (*SEX*), a lot of heavy petting (*SEX*), and we even went to motels and spent some time in bed (*SEX*). The only thing was, I was very afraid of becoming pregnant at that time, therefore we did everything short of intercourse (*IT*). We were doing the forbidden, and it was a lot of fun and exciting, but as I look back it was frustrating rather than satisfying.

"I was engaged while in college and I got birth control pills and had intercourse for the first time. I think that was the most satisfying intercourse ever. (*Fear of pregnancy gone.*) Now there was no fear of parents barging in, invading our privacy, but my husband-to-be had a roommate, and we always thought he might walk in. Or he'd be in the next room. It still seemed sort of forbidden. (*Both she and her husband learned to get off on getting caught, or almost.*)

"I didn't take an active part in sex when I was in college. I just lay there until Tommy got satisfied. Then we got married, and pretty soon we tapered off to maybe once or twice a month. (*Yes, this part should seem familiar. Natasha appeared earlier in the book.*) This was followed by a forced sex situation, where I went off the pill to get pregnant, and that took almost a year. It was terrible. We were forcing ourselves to do something our hearts really weren't into doing. I don't think either one of us were satisfied emotionally. I got uptight about sex. I wasn't getting pregnant and I felt it was something I had to do to *get* pregnant. Then when I did get pregnant, I found I lost most of my interest in sex. After having so little sex, and then so much, now our sex life just about came to a close. I guess it started when I got so trained in my head as a teen-ager to hold back and not fully enjoy what was going on with me sexually because I might get pregnant or someone might find out, or whatever. (*She learned to turn off.*) And then when I got married and it was okay to do that, I was in such a habit of thinking of not fully enjoying myself that maybe I couldn't let go. We'd be going great, and then that fear would set in: 'Oh, my God, we're doing something that'll get me pregnant!' And then I'd shut everything down and wouldn't let myself get any farther into it. I feel all those years of shutting down just kind of became ingrained. (*Yup*).

"Now it's gone a step farther. Before I just lay there, not reacting (*unconscious*), but now I feel pain. I have a reaction to sex, but it is painful. It hurts.

"Maybe it's because I've never experienced orgasm emotionally that I'm not enjoying sex. Not so long ago we tried going to a sex therapist, and he said an orgasm was like a sneeze. He said it builds up and builds up, and it happens, and then after it happens there is this tremendous feeling of relief and release. I never experienced that. I feel a building up of excitement (*Arousal*), which goes to a certain level and I'll be efforting to go higher (*stop straining*), and all of a sudden it's like everything shuts down and I turn off and the area around the clitoris, rather than becoming excited, becomes very sensitive and painful. If I touch it or somebody else touches it, it's uncomfortable or painful. (*How about touching something/somewhere else?*)

"I decided after a while to try it with another man. I put it out to a guy in a sex seminar I went to that I wanted sex, and we did it. And it was really very beautiful. He was divorced and sexually active and he did a lot of different things with me. We did oral sex, and Tommy and I had tried that, but it didn't turn Tommy on, although it turned me on. (*Perhaps Tommy thinks that's dirty; maybe all he needs to know is that it's common, and okay, and Natasha really likes to have him do that.*) He showed me some different positions. The whole experience was very, very neat. But I still didn't have what I call an orgasm. (*She needs to have orgasm defined properly.*) It also proved that it wasn't Tommy. It was me. (*Asset: She's taking responsibility, the first step in taking charge of choices.*)

"What I would like is to be able to fully experience and enjoy sex, including orgasms. That's with my husband and with other people as well if we decided to include other people. I feel I've put up some kind of emotional barrier and I want to do whatever is necessary to *break* down that barrier. (*I'd prefer she walk around the barrier and not break it.*)

"I'm a very realistic person, and it's hard for me to fantasize, get out of the reality. If I work at it, I can conjure something up in the way of a fantasy. I have had dreams involving me in a sexual situation, but I never culminate the situation. I wake up or something happens in the dream, and we don't get that far. I'll be chasing my old boy friend or he'll be chasing me. Sometimes it's Tommy, but usually it's other men. This week I was in a bathtub with another man in my daydream, and we talked about having sex, but we didn't. (*She's stuck in Arousal, which is participation; not even in her daydreams will she participate.*)

"Oh, it's gotten so bad, I worry that it's really all over. We made a deal—we both can have outside affairs, but we can't go to bed with the person more than once. We thought that if we went to bed more than once we might get emotionally involved, and that would jeopardize our marriage. (*As if they didn't have enough silly rules, now they're creating new ones. And she says she has no imagination. Ha!*)

"The problem is, I had one experience with this man named Rick, and I'm afraid I could get emotionally involved. He has moved away, but may move back, and if he does, I don't know how I'll handle that situation at that point. I want to go to bed with him again."

Of course her fantasy involved Rick. (It was included in the chapter about creating productive fantasy, took place in a meadow, and ended with several orgasms, followed by their mutually falling asleep in each other's arms.) She had been instructed by the therapist she'd seen on self-stimulation—something she never had tried before that—and reported some success.

"I experienced something that was better than what I was experiencing before, but I still don't know if the intensity was great enough to call it an orgasm. But I did feel more relaxed than before."

(She asked to watch a videotape to learn what an orgasm was like in another woman. Such tapes are available. She watched and modeled her behavior after that of the woman in the tape. This is observational learning, also referred to as vicarious learning, identification, social facilitation, or imitation. Experiencing an orgasm isn't precisely like changing the spark plugs in a car, or making a dress or shirt from a pattern, but like all activities it may be easier if there is someone present—or on videotape—to show you how it's done and what it looks like, and what it feels like, and how to act. Natasha practiced what she saw and got good at it. She became a winner by

*modeling herself on another winner. Once she experienced
orgasms—and the hurting stopped—she shared them with
her man.)*

MARY JO

*Mary Jo was 31 and head of the women's wear section of
a large department store. She complained of pain due to a
recurrent herpes infection, with sores (blisters, lesions) all
around the vaginal opening.*

"Even before it starts, almost everything in sex play,
except for kissing, I can't be bothered with, or even
interested in. It just doesn't happen in my mind, and I
just hope the whole thing will go away and I get very
irritable. (*Notice that Mary Jo, like so many others, always calls sex "it"—an okay word for solid objects and
bad weather, a rotten word for anything involving repro-
duction/relationship/recreation.*) That's all before it
starts. Then when the touching starts, I start feeling
hostile and I get a feeling of wanting to cry, and then there
is the feeling of holding back and contracting.

"I don't like having my breasts touched, either by hand
or mouth. Somehow that means there's more to come, that
my genitals will be touched and a penis will enter me.
(*She learned to turn off.*) I do not like having my breasts
touched if I know all that is going to happen. (*Could
know that it won't go any further than manual and oral
touch, if her partners agreed.*) I always balk at the genital
area being touched. Why don't I like it? Mainly because
it hurts. I get overly sensitive and frustrated because no
excited feelings come. My body gets rigid, and I cannot
relax. I just get sore and get more of the herpes that I've
had for a year and a half. (*Now, I would ask, what feels
good? Stop dwelling so on what feels lousy. Tell me, what
feels good?*)

"There's a great deal of physical pain, and I know I'm going to have to work extremely hard at relaxing all parts of my body and my mind so it won't hurt as much. When I finally relax, which takes about five minutes, the man is able to move in and out a little bit easier. (*Asset: She knows how to relax, a skill that may be used in many ways.*) He can stay in for five, ten, fifteen minutes at a time until the pain gets unbearable again. And then we have to stop. I usually end up making the male come with either my hand or my mouth. It will vary on how I'm feeling or how sore I am as to whether the guy will help me get an orgasm. Some of the time we don't even try to get me to have an orgasm as I'm sore, uptight with myself, and depressed about the entire incident.

"I might add that I've never felt any physical pleasure or excitement with a penis inside me. (*Yet.*) I just don't trust men. (*Does she want to?*) It's not okay somehow to totally be giving to them. It makes me feel vulnerable, that they have some kind of power over me, that they can hurt me both physically and mentally.

"When and how often does this problem occur? Gee, almost every time that serious lovemaking takes place. I'm fine as long as I'm fooling around and playing and teasing, but all of a sudden when something clicks, and I realize that this is for real, I start to freeze. (*She shuts down just like Natasha.*)

"Once in a while when my sex drive is strong enough, it will be easy. It's like I'm chemically easy and it doesn't matter where my mind is. (*Assets: It works perfectly sometimes, could again; she's already experienced her goal. Also, there is no sex "drive"—only readiness.*)

"The problem always occurs if I'm anywhere but on a bed, usually my bed, because I live on my bed. Not just with sex, but with everything. When I need to read, rest, talk, sometimes eat, I'm always on my bed. I always have been. I like to be as comfortable mentally and physically as possible if I know I'm going to make love. (*Asset: She likes sex in bed. Most people do. It sounds to me as if she's ready for sex much of the time. Her bedroom fascination is okay. A creature of habit is someone who has learned well. A person who learns well can learn more—easily.*)

"I've always had this problem. I don't remember it not being there except for about six months of my life about three years ago, which was right after my divorce. I was twenty-eight and we'd been married for eight years. Then, after we split up, all of a sudden I was going out with five men at the same time and going to bed with three of them. I was pretty much enjoying myself—once in a while having an orgasm, once in a while by their giving it to me and once in a while giving it to myself. Most of the time I wasn't worrying about it. I was feeling good about it and having a good time. I was feeling natural. (*There's that word again.*) No moral trips. I still held back some, but not nearly so much as had always been the case before. (*Asset: Did work before, could work again.*)

"How have I handled the problem? The whole range. I've worried about it, felt inadequate, went to not caring, ignored it. The main way I handled it was to not get myself into any situations where I felt it might come up. To totally escape it. (*Herpes permits escaping.*) Before the marriage I used the I can't-do-anything-because-I'm-not-married bit as an excuse. (*Rules!*) I was still a virgin three days after I was married. Plus, we had lived together for a year before that.

"The second or third night of our marriage, something hit me that something was wrong. I had really thought that I'd want to make love as soon as I was married, but that piece of paper hadn't changed anything. I tried to relax and enjoy the whole thing, but I couldn't, so each time it would turn into a bad experience. The times of trying got farther and farther apart. We talked about the problems and decided my senses just didn't feel things easily. Also, we were both inexperienced and neither of us knew what to do in lovemaking. Besides that, his penis was really big and I used the excuse that my vagina was really small. (*The vagina is really a potential space, small enough to inhibit the passage of a finger, large enough to permit the passage of a ten-pound baby at the conclusion of pregnancy.*) And one of the main things was, I was always getting vaginal infections every time we had intercourse.

"After five years of an unhappy marriage, I started going to family guidance counseling on how to get the marriage together. I tried to get my husband to go, but he felt it was my problem. I went there for a year. Instead of helping the marriage and our nonexistent sex life, it made me strong enough to ask for a divorce.

"As far as where I learned about sex, at seventeen I started going steady with a guy and we were constantly kissing. Finally, after about four months, he touched my breast and that was a huge conflict. I liked it really a lot, but I was totally mortified that he'd know how small-busted I was because I was wearing a padded bra. The same night I threw it away and never wore one again. I carried that feeling with me. I wasn't big-busted enough, I wasn't okay, I was always thin. (*Liability: Counting size, not sighs.*) I've pretty well gotten over it, but once in a while it comes back.

"When I was twenty, I went with a guy for a while, did the whole kissing bit and he touched my breasts and wanted me to touch his penis. I'd never thought of consciously touching him. I didn't know I was supposed to. (*Rules!*) After letting that sink in, I started touching him. It was really hard to do. And that's what our relationship basically ended up as. He never got to touch my genitals. Somehow I had that feeling then that if I let him touch me, that meant we'd have to go all the way.

"Then I met the man I married, and we lived together for a year. We kissed a lot and rolled around and he touched my breasts, but he was not allowed to get inside me. Not until we were married. He went along with it. Then came the marriage and the whole revelation that I didn't want a penis inside me, that it hurt, that it brought up a lot of wanted and unwanted feelings, such as fear, hate, love, pain, and pleasure all at once. I couldn't cope with it, so I slowly cut off any of the good feelings I had. (*Liability: She's stopped participating. Asset: But she's just like Natasha. The great power in "shutting down" can be used to turn on as well.*)

"My husband and I had started experimenting with oral sex, which led me to doing him more to keep him away from me. After I succeeded in keeping him happy and he would have a climax, he would go to sleep. Which was what I wanted all the time. But deep down I was angry and hating, and hurting that he couldn't help me in my problems. (*Readiness: She knows it could work, with his assistance.*)

"For what it's worth, I feel most of the problems stem from my parent's divorce when I was three, and my mother laying the you-can't-trust-men and you-don't-marry-for-love-just-security trips on me. Plus my stepfather. I was five when they married and I remember literally freezing if he wanted me to sit on his lap or he tried to hug or kiss me in a fatherly way. I knew he wasn't my father and it wasn't okay. (*Liability: She blames others. She is ir-response-able. Could adopt a positive point of view immediately and begin to win. Could become response-able—able to respond, to be orgasmic, to be alive, fully aroused, fully participatory—or could continue as she is and lose.*)

"I learned about masturbation in the sixth grade in health class, but I only knew that boys did it. I didn't learn that it was okay for girls to do. I didn't even connect it up that I might try to do it. I didn't think about it or try it until I was twenty or twenty-one. But all it did was get me frustrated and I quit until I was twenty-six. (*She didn't know* how *to do it.*) At that time I was fully into women's liberation and was wanting a divorce and had just read *The Sensuous Woman*, and was getting a lot about different women's feelings about their sexual life, and their body, and what they were feeling was common to them. So I tried masturbating and after a few days of trying I had an orgasm by direct stimulation, using my hands. I didn't have to touch myself the rest of the night but I had over fifty orgasms. (*Yippee.*) I was so over-whelmed by that that it was two weeks before I tried it again. This time I had twenty-five orgasms. I was really pleased with myself." (*Asset: She might wish to involve someone else now.*)

Mary Jo is to be congratulated and nurtured for moving from Leftsidedness toward Rightsidedness, but from what she fantasizes below (another familiar tape excerpt, used before), it still isn't quite enough. She doesn't want fifty orgasms alone. She wants one, without pain, with a friend.

"My love and I are hugging, kissing, touching, laughing. I see me making him come with my hands and mouth, making him feel good. And then he's doing the same to me. Then I see him entering me without any pain and just making love in any number of positions. I don't see any particular positions, just doing whatever comes natur-ally. What mainly is happening, though, is the total love feeling, the energy vibrations, me feeling that things are being done to me and moving freely when I feel the good feelings. And making sound come out and nothing feels like it's being held back. Where none of that old junk comes in—all of that shit that I keep having to go through my mind and my body. None of that is happening. We are just being."

Mary Jo needed to notice her assets, to do what the old Johnny Mercer song said: "Ac-cent-tchu-ate the positive, e-lim-eye-nate the negative." A handy way of doing this is to review the tape, writing down only the good stuff. For example, Mary Jo's tape includes the following:

"When I finally relax, which takes about five minutes, the man is able to move in and out a little bit easier. He can stay in for five, ten, fifteen minutes . . .

"I usually (make) the male come with either my hand or my mouth.

"I'm fine as long as I'm fooling around and playing and teasing . . .

". . . when my sex drive is strong enough, it will be easy.

"I like to be as comfortable mentally and physically as possible . . .

"I was pretty much enjoying myself—once in a while having an orgasm, once in a while by their giving it to me and once in a while giving it to myself. Most of the time I wasn't worrying about it. I was feeling good about it and having a good time. I was feeling natural. No moral trips.

". . . we were constantly kissing.

"My husband and I had started experimenting with oral sex . . .

"I learned about masturbation in the sixth grade in health class . . ." *(And on and on it goes, straight through 50 orgasms with no hands and a fantastic, creative fantasy. No one has ever sounded so much a winner.*

As it happened, Mary Jo left her partner, and her painful herpes went away. She wrote months later to let me know that she believed she was moving into a good "place"— literally and figuratively, an ashram in California. And she was experiencing orgasm every time she participated in sexual activity.)

SANDRA

Sandra was 23, first experienced sex at 16, and married the man a year later. She worked part time as a market researcher.

"What brought me here was a sexual problem. I'm having pain during intercourse, which is causing me to not be interested in having intercourse with my husband. The pain started following an automobile accident, where, besides a broken tailbone and ribs, I suffered injuries to my vagina. Just outside the opening I was torn, which caused me to bleed a lot and I had to have surgery. When I went back for my checkup after leaving the hospital, the examination was extremely painful. I remember being on this X-ray table with all these doctors in the room. I didn't feel like a person, just like an object. One of the doctors introduced himself and he didn't try to examine me because he knew it hurt. But another doctor did. The pain was terrible, I couldn't believe the pain.

"I think the incident in the hospital and my injuries to myself have a lot to do with my problem. But I'm not sure that I'm not just using it to cover up how I feel about other things. (*I'll buy that.*) I'm not certain if I love my husband or if he loves me. Now when I have intercourse with my husband I feel like an object, and he doesn't care how I feel. I can really be turned on and then I just stop everything inside me and I can't enjoy it. (Asset: *She's just like Natasha and Mary Jo—able to switch off, powerfully.*)

"Things he does really aggravate me, and that resentment seems to block how I feel in bed with him. He acts like it's too much trouble to take time with our son, and when he does he usually criticizes. (*He's selfish.*) And he never says 'our' son. He always says 'my' son, and 'my' car, and 'my' future. Always singular. I always ask, 'What about me?'

"He didn't come on like the other guys I dated. He was shy. It was two weeks before he even put his arm around me. I kind of felt secure. I was brought up in the Catholic religion and very strict parents. My dad had been illegitimate, and I kind of felt like he was afraid I'd do something wrong. He loved me, I think, but he never showed me enough. I think back now and I know he had problems of his own. My brother died before I was born. Then I came along—sickly all the time. I guess they were afraid something would happen to me, too. Dad never got his boy again—only five girls. I tried to please him. I went out for basketball, but he never came and watched me play.

"My experiences with sex . . . I remember when I was five years old and I walked in when my dad was taking a bath. He was in the tub. I couldn't see anything, but I remember the shock on his face when he saw me. He called for my mother to come and get me out of there. I couldn't understand at the time what the big deal was all about.

"The first sexual experience was with my husband-to-be. I was sixteen and, I don't know, I really didn't like it. I felt guilty afterwards and I guess I still do, because I did it before I was married, and that was always something I was taught not to do. Nice girls didn't do that, and I was a really nice girl. (*Liability: She's got flypaper in her files —a picture from when she was sixteen is stuck to last night's attempt at "intercourse." And she doesn't know that it's possible to be a nice girl and do it, too.*)

"Right now I couldn't care less about having sex with my husband. I think we went through most of our marriage where I pretended that I enjoyed it. (*In royal circles, pretenders to the throne rarely enjoy king- and queen-sized pleasures.*) Maybe it's because I felt guilty, the way I was brought up and was told, I guess, like, when you get married and you really love the guy, you just want to do everything for him, and everything is supposed to be oh, so perfect. (*And it wasn't perfect, so she concluded something was wrong. Most people don't question the myth, questioning themselves instead.*) Sometimes just before we have intercourse I fantasize that, or I think that I'm really getting into it and then it doesn't work and, oh, I feel so frustrated. I can't understand why we were always told or always thought it would be a certain way, and it wasn't.

"I want more kids, but then I don't. If I felt I was doing everything right with the only one that I have, then maybe. There's so much to raising a kid. If I had been raised differently, then maybe I wouldn't have so many problems and maybe doing so many things wrong with my son's life. (*Liability: She isn't taking responsibility, is blaming Mom and Dad.*)

"I think . . . well, I wonder what it would be like to have intercourse with someone else. My husband's told me he's never had intercourse with anyone else, but I don't believe him because I found a letter that he'd written a girl, and I felt like I was betrayed.

"Each time it usually was one of his friends that'd come on to me. Like when he was in Vietnam, his supposedly best friend who was married and they were expecting a baby, and I trusted that he was just trying to be nice and friendly and trying to console me while my husband was gone, well, he kissed me and that was as far as I let it go, but I felt guilty about it. And then about a year ago, when we were having trouble, again it was a friend of my husband's who told me that he loved me. I didn't believe him. I thought he was just after what he could get. I never let it go farther than a kiss each time. I liked it, but then I felt guilty afterwards.

"When I think about what it would be like with somebody else, I think I really would like to try it, because I feel like I'll have missed something to go through all my life just having intercourse with my husband. I feel guilty when I have these thoughts."

(Sandra was an ir-response-able woman, declining to take control of her life—feeling guilty about premarital sex, blaming an auto accident and Mom and Dad and society for the flaws in her partnership, dreaming about having an affair and feeling guilty about that. I noticed that she never mentioned the word "orgasm" and asked if she had them. She said no. I told her she had a choice— she could be sexually responsive and satisfied, or not, as she wished. She and her partner weren't communicating. ["I'm not certain if I love my husband or if he loves me."] I suggested they talk to each other. They did, and she learned to get in touch with her feelings and doings, learned to experience orgasm through self-stimulation, practiced with her husband. They're still together. And it doesn't hurt now.)

CHAPTER

16

"I'm / She's So Small We Can't Do It"

When dyspareunia (painful intercourse) is severe it can be associated with what the muscles have learned to do best in the presence of pain—contract. A broken bone is associated in the area of the break with severe muscle spasm. When an eye responds to the pain of something within, it responds the way it knows how: by having its circular musculature close. So we see an eye squinting and tearing. A vagina does the same in the presence of pain—it contracts. And it can learn to contract so that when anything comes near it—the speculum of a gynecologist, a finger of a physician, or the penis of a partner—it goes into spasm. Severe muscle contraction is called *vaginismus*.

Masters and Johnson, in *Human Sexual Inadequacy*, point toward their 100-percent cure rate using the "Haslam technique": slowly stretching the vagina's entrance with a graduated series of dilators. Other therapists suggest using first the little finger, then a larger finger, then two, then three. Whatever the method, this is an easy complaint to fix.

It may occur for the most interesting reasons. Polly, for example, was the oldest of nine children, and because both her parents worked at two jobs, she was totally responsible for raising all her younger brothers and sisters. "Since then," she said, "I've developed some very negative ideas about having my own children." Her husband, meantime, insisted she might one day change her mind. She answered that challenge by creating the perfect cop-out. She denied him intercourse, telling him that it was only because her vagina wouldn't let her. This is typical. The pain is real, yet there is no physical reason for it.

Sometimes there *is* a physical reason. Tanya was 14 when her parents brought her in. She was one of several I've seen over the years who had only a dimple where the vagina should be.

I had been trained in a traditional procedure to create a vagina surgically. When doctors do this, they develop a balsa or styrofoam phallus. With the woman under anesthetic they make an incision where the vagina ought to be and, through blunt dissection, they create the potential space. They then take a split-thickness graft from a portion of the person's skin and invert it over the phallus. Now the skin side envelops the phallus and the moist subcutaneous tissue is outside the phallus. You insert this into the blunt space you had dissected and you figure out a way to keep it in. The graft would now take—you hope —against the sides of the new vagina and, interestingly, as the graft (or most of it) took, over time it would not have the appearance of dry skin inside. Instead, it would have the appearance of mucous membrane.

I had learned how to do this and had used it on a number of occasions with women who had no vaginas. Even with the best results, there was the possibility of contracture. Unless you kept the balsa phallus in for a long time, what you created might contract down and become foreshortened and stricturized. A way to prevent this, of course, was continuing dilatation through intercourse. You couldn't very well suggest this as part of a 14-year-old's postoperative recovery, however, so the practice was to delay surgery until just before the young woman married. And that presented more problems. The terrible thing about waiting was that people felt abnormal, and when you feel abnormal, you don't get into dating situations easily.

I told Tanya's parents about a mechanical procedure. I told her to go home and twice a day exert pressure against the dimple with her finger. She came back to see me every two weeks, and six weeks later she had a nine-centimeter (three-and-a-half-inch) vagina, which not only was truly remarkable of itself; it had the pliancy that you never would see following surgery. And Tanya wasn't atypical. I've treated lots of Tanyas.

My approach is to tell Tanya's story to every woman with vaginismus. Not to say, "Look, lady, Tanya didn't even *have* a vagina . . ." No, no—I want to say, "Lady, look, you're hope-empty right now. Every time you've tried it, it hasn't worked. And it hasn't worked because the very, very first time you had intercourse it hurt. It hurt cerebrally, it hurt vaginally, and your muscles did what muscles know how to do in reaction to pain."

Tanya's story usually makes the women at least hope-more; often they get hopefull. Dilators and fingers are introduced. And in the meantime, if it seems appropriate, the woman is told about self-stimulation and orgasm from touching *outside*. Intercourse is suspended until the woman and her vagina are ready—and in the meantime other satisfying behavior is tried.

CHAPTER

17

"I Come Too Fast"

Neither of these full-bodied males about to be described ever started his timers at the start of arousal. Each pushed the button at the moment of penetration.

Both, of course, are normal. Each experiences desire, arousal, and orgasm. Each evaluates his "performance" as less than adequate, lacking, somehow failing. They expect to be put down by their partners. They believe that women want to be subjected to "endless, timeless pounding." They adopt the same competitive attitude that runs them in their businesses, and even though they can't tell you *who* they are competing with, they *know* the other guys are "better" (last longer). Each has learned to be a loser.

In general, all noncoital activity, whether practiced alone or in the presence of or with another, need never be timed and in fact, with most people, hardly ever is.

BERT

Bert was 29 and an aggressive real estate salesman in one of southern California's top agencies. He was married five years. There were no children.

"The problem, stated very simply, is that my wife and I, for a man and woman of our age, don't have sex very often. This problem spreads itself throughout our marriage. I know that eventually this will probably be more of a problem than it is now. (*Watch it, Bert, this could turn into self-fulfilling prophecy.*) We still enjoy each other's company. We still, seemingly at least, are happy with each other. In every way our marriage seems to be very good, except for this problem of performing sexually.

"When we do have sex, I don't think it's particularly fulfilling for either of us, though. (*When was the last time it was? Describe it. You could re-create this "did" if you wish.*) But the last few times we've had it I don't think I've been particularly motivated to doing it again very soon. (*It's probably not much fun.*) I don't know whether it's my wife's problem or mine. But we really haven't enjoyed it. I feel that we really both have the problem. (*And part of the problem is calling it "it."*)

"I don't know where or when it started, but when we discuss this we take mutual blame. I think my wife feels a little more that it's my problem, basically. At least she feels I started the problem. I don't know that that's true and I don't know that she feels that strongly anymore. (*Ask her.*) The problem is a constant problem. We don't have it very often, and honestly I don't remember very well how often we do have it. (*He's really unconscious.*) But I know that we don't have it any more than once every four to six months. (*By everyone's standards that does seem infrequent.*)

"I noticed a certain lack of sexual interest shortly after we were married. We've been married over five years, and it seems that not long after we were married, sex just didn't seem to have the excitement we had prior to our marriage. It just didn't seem the same. (*Well, for one thing, it was no longer forbidden, Bert.*)

"I think that we have decided that the time to go to bed is the time to go to sleep. For whatever reason, this has been instilled into us, and we do go to sleep. Both my wife and myself, especially my wife, love sleeping. We really do enjoy sleeping. She has instilled this in me. I used to believe that sleeping was a waste of time, but I have changed my opinion, where I really do enjoy going to bed and going to sleep. (*Good. Now consider making love away from your bed.*) My energy level is not particularly high, for that matter. I'm not particularly active anymore, and this could be one of the reasons why I go to bed to go to sleep. (*Excuses, excuses. The truth is, you don't have to "perform" when you're asleep.*)

"We're trying to get back to the what I would consider normal sexual activity for people our age . . . not even just our age, it's just I don't feel as sexually active as I should be. (*"Shoulds" are rules and Leftsided. "Coulds" are possibilities and Rightsided.*)

"There's nothing wrong with our marriage except this sexual problem. If we can get rid of it, there's no question in my mind that we'll have an A-100 terrific marriage. I want us to be happy and to go to bed (*we may have to begin elsewhere*) and make love to one another. We're very good friends. I love my wife very much. I think we should show that more affectionately. I would very much like to develop a really live sexual activity. I believe sex should be part of two human beings being together. As much as I love being with my wife, I can't help but think if we weren't married as long as we've been together, almost any woman I was living with, I'd have sexual activity more often. I feel there is a barrier there. I feel it is un-natural if we don't have sex. (*There's that word "natural" again.*) I hope to break down whatever inhibitions are there that keep us apart sexually. I don't feel my wife or I have any unusual sexual aspects. I feel like I'm a normal American male and the same for my wife. (*He's ready!*)

"I don't recall either my mother or my father ever talking about sex with me. The birds and bees talk never occurred. What I learned I learned on the streets with my friends—the dirty jokes, the meetings at friends' houses, the sexual activities there, whatever, I just learned by whatever happened. I don't think any negative things about sex were said or shown to me. I don't feel sex is wrongful or harmful in any way. I do feel that perversions —male/male and female/female relationships—are wrong. I am liberal enough to know that certain individuals do have that kind of relationship and it's okay, so long as it doesn't affect me.

"I've been embarrassed for most of my life about the size of my penis. (*Aha!*) It's small by standards (*whose?*) and in its soft or flaccid state it is very small. As I've grown into adulthood, it has grown somewhat, but it's still small in its flaccid state. (*So what! Of what use is a large flaccid penis?*) When erect it's more toward what I've read is a normal size. My penis is about five inches long when erect, and I would assume that six is about normal. (*No, no. Five and four and three are "normal" too.*) However, early in my athletic career, taking showers with other guys my age, I began to realize that most of them were considerably larger than I was. (*It always seems so, but only because you're looking down at yours and across at theirs, and the perspective alters perception.*) I remember one particular fellow pointed at me one day, we were in the fourth or fifth grade, and he said, 'Aren't you ever going to grow up—you're still like a baby.' (*This fourth grade picture from Bert's file is stuck to today's picture.*)

It was true. And to this day, my penis is small. (*Really only smaller than you want it to be.*) That's probably pretty influential with sexual activity with girls. I've been embarrassed to be seen in the flaccid state. By the time I am aroused, it takes on much less importance, but I'm always conscious of it with my wife. I know that since the advent of new magazines and probably previous sexual activity that she knows that men's penises are often larger than mine. (*Maybe she's only experienced smaller ones, Bert. That's possible, too, you know.*) Then again, other girls' boobs are often larger than my wife's. (*Boy, is he into the numbers game. The* Playboy *Advisor had the final word about penis size: "It's not the size of the wand that puts the rabbit in the hat; it's the magic of the performer."*)

"During my forming years, sexually I was plagued with what I would refer to as premature ejaculation . . . never quite getting to the sex act prior to ejaculation. This may have kept me out of trouble and kept me out of being married to some girl I absolutely despise now, I'm not sure. (*Another rule: Get pregnant, get married.*) So I never got the sexual experience I would like to have.

"I do become excited and do ejaculate sooner than she is excited and so, therefore, we do not reach climax together often. (*Almost no one does.*) Occasionally we do. (*Now there's a "did."*) But usually I'm excited and come before she does, and after that I'm pretty much finished for the evening. It ends up in a fairly frustrated state for her, I'm sure. (*Even after orgasming he could continue to stimulate his wife, orally, manually, etc.*)

"My sexual experiences have been few and far between, and generally I'd say they were frustrating. I haven't really made love to many girls. Now, as I look back on it, that's kind of a bummer, because I'm sure I would have experienced various girls and techniques and whatever, maybe even have learned more about what turns me on, so I could

help my wife along these lines. (*He's playing "if only."
He's stuck in the "didn'ts" and ignoring the "coulds."*)
Examples of my sexual experiences . . . I'll start with the
child sex games, showing each other the various parts
of our bodies. I enjoyed the hell out of it, but I remember
an elderly aunt caught us. She didn't stop us at that time,
but we were told later that she thought it was bad and
shabby. I have practiced masturbation for a long time. I
was told by someone much better endowed than myself
in penis size that masturbation would help my penis grow.
So I practiced it regularly. (*Asset: He knows how to
practice.*) He was wrong, my penis didn't grow, but I
learned to feel good. I have masturbated most of my life.
(*With what thoughts? He could masturbate and think that
his penis was really okay from his wife's point of view.*)

"My encounters with the opposite sex started in the
sixth grade. I went with a girl with huge mammary glands.
I remember avid sexual activity with her—playing with
her boobs, rubbing each other. But I was very embarrassed
by the size of my penis and never allowed her to put her
hand on me so she could feel the size of it. I've only had
one same-sex encounter. It happened when I was very
young, and a boy about a year older than I was tried to
enter my anus with his penis. I didn't like that at all. Not
that I was turned off. I was bored. I don't think I was
penetrated. (*Unconscious again?*)

"My first actual sexual intercourse occurred when I
was in college, in a whorehouse. It was just kind of dull.
My next was with the girl who is now my wife. We enjoyed it tremendously. (*Notice that your wife enjoyed—
"small" weenie and all. This is a "did" that could be re-
created.*) We got a motel room and spent the whole night
together. (*When was the last time you were in a motel
with your wife?*) The next girl was a barfly waitress type,
who really seduced me more than I seduced her. It was a
relatively neat experience except that I was terribly hung

over the next day and I wasn't sure how it turned out. I think it might have developed into more if I hadn't had so much to drink.

"It's embarrassing now that I have to masturbate while fantasizing to enjoy some sexual activity. My fantasies do disturb me somewhat, but more than that is the fact that my loving wife is in the next room available to me when I am masturbating. (*He could join her in the next room and share with her what he learned.*)

"My sexual fantasies usually involve another girl, not the same girl every time—a girl I know, a friend of my wife's, generally a girl I think is available to me. There doesn't seem to be a set pattern as to what the girl looks like, or the environment. The only thing I would say is the sexual activity is very much in private. I would hate the risk of being caught. And there is a certain feeling of her seducing me. I'm more than willing, but she makes the first move.

"An ideal sexual relationship for me is very, very difficult to describe. The girl involved would be attractive and would be very turned on to me. She would be frightfully happy that I had made love to her. It would involve my having a larger penis, one which she is impressed with. (*Still playing the numbers game. He could realize that she could be impressed with his penis as is.*) It would end in mutual orgasm and a real contentment afterwards, a feeling of sharing an enjoyable experience.

"I guess that's about it. I could go on and expound in some areas, but it's taken me an hour and forty minutes to make this (*35-minute*) tape. Part of that has been going back and listening to what I've said. I do feel better for having made the tape. It has been interesting to listen back to see what I have to say."

(*Bert didn't know that his wife knew about his masturbatory habits. Nor did he really know how his "secret" masturbation could serve him well. It hadn't occurred to*

*him that in general, all noncoital activity, whether prac-
ticed alone or in the presence of (or with) another, need
never be timed and in fact, with most people, hardly ever
was. I asked him, "Do you come 'prematurely' when you
masturbate?" Bert was given an opportunity to listen to
an audiotape, "Learning self-stimulation—male version."
Some excerpts, showing him how to improve his "staying
power" manually, follow.)*

DR.:　　　The thing to remember is that as you learn
more about your own sexual response pattern
through self-stimulation, you can become more
comfortable with your body and more comfortable about sharing pleasure with your partner.

MR. A.:　　That's certainly been so for me. Practicing self-
stimulation has allowed me to learn more about
what particular sexual stimuli turn me on, has
allowed me to experience my orgasm in a more
relaxed and comfortable way. I've been able to
share and communicate this with my wife, and
our sexual relationship has really benefited.
You know, on those occasions when I'm away
from my wife, like on business trips, or when
I'm aroused and she's not, I've used self-
stimulation as a very sexually fulfilling experience.

DR.:　　　That's perfect. In practicing self-stimulation,
what did you find important?

MR. A.:　　Well, I noticed that one of the most important
things is to find a comfortable setting, a place
where you can have privacy and not be interrupted, where you know you won't be disturbed. It's important to make sure you're
not tired, that you have plenty of time. I found

that the bathroom or the bedroom were the most enjoyable places. I've got to tell you the truth though, I had some hesitation at first— I guess that's what you meant by, "It takes time to learn, and especially a lot of the new things we want to learn."

DR.: Yes, that's very true, but let's review some of the techniques which others have found to be positive. Mr. Abbott, many men choose to begin by massaging their bodies with a favorite body lotion or an oil . . . just enjoying the touch of their skin. In fact, it often helps to close your eyes and imagine a special person or place from your past, a movie setting, a book, or anything else that might be arousing to you.

MR. A.: It's funny. I knew that many men looked at erotic pictures, I didn't know that happily married men actually engaged in self-stimulation while they did that.

DR.: Right, many men find erotic materials and fantasy very stimulating. The important thing is to relax, think about what makes you feel aroused. Once you are relaxed, you may want to begin to explore your body to find out what different sensations are produced by a variety of movements of the fingers and of the hands. As you begin stroking, caressing your genital area, see what feels most positive. Experiment and notice how the intensity of the feelings, the sensations begin to change.

You may use feathers, textured materials, clothing, virtually anything you find arousing. Vibrators are another alternative. They can be purchased at department and drug stores.

Should you wish some assistance about that, ask your doctor. Some men find that the sensation of vibration placed on the penis, the testicles, or in the anal region heightens arousal and facilitates orgasm.

MR. A.:   I had heard that some men fantasize women other than their partners during masturbation. I learned that this particular behavior doesn't really enhance my marital relationship. I found out that it was much more appropriate to place my wife, my partner, in my imagination during self-stimulation, especially at the moment of orgasm. You know that was one of the beneficial things I've learned, especially when I was away from home and felt aroused.

DR.:   That's so important. The most effective moment to think of your partner is during your orgasm.

MR. A.:   I also do it, by the way, when I'm having sexual relations with my wife. We've both found that it is very enhancing to our sexual life. I've learned to use self-stimulation to expand our sexual relationship while we're together, also, so that I'm now more aware of my own body and my own pleasures.

(This was perfect advice for Bert. He continued to masturbate. At first alone, adopting some of these suggestions, slowly extending the length of time by stopping whenever he approached orgasm—something he found easier to do than when experiencing intercourse. He began to create a productive fantasy, getting a picture of his wife as he did this, imagining himself actually experiencing longer and longer periods of intercourse, rewarding

these thoughts with an orgasm. In time, he began stimulating himself with his wife present. She often had masturbated to orgasm, too, and she joined him. They began stimulating each other manually. Intercourse followed. Problem solved.)

PAUL

Paul was 33, production manager of a small electronics factory, and married to Doreen for ten years. The incidence of sexual intercourse was down to once a month when he came in and, like Bert and many other men who feel inadequate, he approached his problem obliquely.

"My wife lacks interest in having sex. (*Obviously she doesn't have fun.*) She was never what I would call passionate in the sex department since we married. However, it's only recently that her desire has been to reduce our sex life. My wife is a very emotional person, and approximately six months ago she was very depressed and advised me that sex was dirty and that we'd been married ten years, and she saw no need to continue to have sex, and if I thought sex was important I should seek satisfaction elsewhere.

"I don't expect to have sexual relations at any particular rate. That is, I don't expect it to be once a week or twice a week or whatever. But I do desire having a partner who enjoys sex from time to time. And I've got the impression over the years that there's not any mutual interest. This is a terrific deterrent. Because, although my wife isn't inclined to reject me when I make an advance toward her, knowing she's not interested causes me not to make advances. I don't look at sex as a way of satisfying only myself. That is part of it, I enjoy that and I get a lot of satisfaction. But if I haven't satisfied her or she isn't enjoying it, it's an incomplete feeling and therefore I'm not making the advances I would otherwise make if I felt she was enthusiastic about it. (*He really wants to be otherish about sex, but doesn't know what could make her enthusiastic. He could learn.*)

"I had a difficulty when we were first married in bringing my wife to climax. In fact, I don't think I've ever brought her to a climax while having intercourse. This was very frustrating for me. I felt very inadequate. I felt I had a problem of what is called 'premature ejaculation.' (*How long would you have to last from the moment of entry in order to consider yourself a "postmature ejaculator?"*) Therefore I tried all ways of controlling it, but I was never able to get my wife sexually aroused enough to have a climax in the desired manner. (*He probably bit the inside of his cheek, counted backward, thought about garbage, or did one of a hundred other things that take you away from sex rather than into it. This is not getting tuned in or turned on; it is merely dropping out.*)

"I was able to solve the problem to some extent by bringing her to a climax through manipulation with my hand (*could have done this during intercourse*) or through oral manipulation before I had intercourse. This way I felt I had satisfied her and then I'd satisfy myself. This was a pattern that we fell into over the years and it seemed to be the best available solution. (*Of course it isn't the only available solution. Only Paul and his wife can say what's "best."*) I wasn't totally satisfied, but on the other hand it was reasonably satisfactory to me, and I thought the same was true for my wife until she indicated a complete disinterest.

"I want to bring her to climax through intercourse by increasing her ability to have a climax or by increasing my ability to help through foreplay or whatever. Maybe even she can climax during intercourse. (*Readiness: He recognizes the possibilities. And it's easy if she wants to and is willing to learn.*)

"I learned about sex in the way that most teen-aged boys do. I had some older friends who while swimming masturbated, and I learned about that. I started necking with girls when I was twelve or thirteen. Heavy petting followed at fifteen. While I was a junior in high school at sixteen, I became emotionally involved and had intercourse for the first time. I was completely inexperienced and it probably wasn't very satisfying for either of us. (*What does "probably" mean? Speak for yourself, Paul.*) I had infrequent relationships in college and after. There were about ten girls from sixteen to twenty-eight, when I married. None of the relationships were ideal. (*I wonder what would have been.*)

"While I was younger I didn't have a place of my own to live. While I was going to school the relationships were almost always in the back seat or front seat of an automobile, which of course tends to rush the whole process. (*Liability: A classic factor in the history of the typical quick trigger.*) It wasn't until I moved to Hawaii and lived here two years, before I was married, that I became involved with one charming girl, and that relationship was quite satisfactory and I believe I was able to satisfy her. She had a considerable enthusiasm for sex. But she also had guilt feelings about the propriety of it since we weren't married. She'd feel we should discontinue, and it'd take a lot of persuasion on my part. (*Liability: Another classic factor—he feels he must experience penetration and ejaculation before she changes her mind about letting him.*)

"So I wasn't a fully experienced partner and I may not have introduced my wife, who I believe had no experience, to sex in what would be considered the most favorable manner. I probably should've been more patient and understood more about bringing women to climaxes. Making sure that they enjoyed it and so on. I feel this contributed to my wife's lack of enjoyment. I just hope it isn't too late to correct the situation. (*It isn't from my point of view, Paul. Let's make sure to ask your wife.*)

"My early involvements were generally ordinary. I had two experiences with experienced girls. With the first I reached a very early climax (*how early?*) and she complained. I was twenty-three or so. It hurt my ego, and I didn't react constructively and shortly thereafter the relationship ended. I had a similar experience with a stewardess. We had sex twice, neither time performing to her expectation, and she made gentle comments about that.

"There haven't been any serious affairs since I got married. There were some extramarital affairs when I was traveling, maybe half a dozen times with prostitutes over ten years. It was more for a lack of opportunity than anything else; I didn't get involved. I don't think the problem is so serious that I'd be embarrassed about performance. I'd gladly have gotten involved if I had had an opportunity, when I got depressed about my home life. In the business I'm in I don't get to meet many women and I would never approach one of the secretaries, because of the complications.

"I want to correct the situation. I don't want to develop outside relationships. My marriage would suffer." (*Purposefullness: He knows what he wants.*)

(*Paul was caught in the "premature ejaculator's" classic double bind. Since he always knew he was a "quick trigger," he was certain that all during the marriage the real reason why she wasn't enjoying sex was because he was a quick trigger—and that of course only aggravated the* problem. He believed that when she told him she didn't want to experience sex with him anymore, that just proved he was a failure.

They came to see me together, and I noticed that masturbation was not an okay topic. Immediately I asked her if their little girls touched themselves. She noticed that they did and she got all shook and then laughed because she noticed that she did it now and she'd always done it and experienced orgasm doing it. She agreed to share this activity with her husband, showing him how to do it. He got over his hang-up about thinking it was his fault that she didn't come. The truth is, once she took responsibility for her coming, he began to enjoy her and they got "well."

I also suggested to Paul what I suggest to all men who have this complaint: Do it more often. You see, many therapists—including Masters and Johnson—generally recommend what is called the "squeeze technique," where manual pressure is applied to the glans of the penis when the male feels ejaculation is near. Then stimulation is resumed until ejaculation is again imminent, when the penis is again tightly squeezed. The idea is that over a period of time the male learns to delay his orgasm. However effective this technique has proved to be, this seems negative, even aversive to me. I prefer positive conditioning. Most "premature ejaculators" tend to avoid sex—for fear of failing again—and I tell them to do the opposite: Do it again and again and again. I believe that if the "premature ejaculator" would increase the frequency of sexual activity with another, he could last longer, especially if he has experienced this in the past—i.e., taking longer to come the third, fourth, or fifth times in a weekend.

I believe in setting up the couple to win. I ask the female to do whatever is customary so that her partner becomes aroused, then suggest that she make him come as quickly as possible for more times than usual during a 72-hour period. The result is as predictable as sunshine in Hawaii:

The fourth or fifth or whatever time, the man's penis is hard and he's saying, "I can't come . . . I can't come . . ." And then it's time for a quiet, satisfied nap. For "premature ejaculators," more is definitely better.)

CHAPTER

18

"I Can't Come at All"

THERESA

Theresa was 36 and operated a natural foods restaurant with her husband of 12 years. They had two children.

"My problem is one of being able to achieve orgasm. Also, we have a very low level of sexual activity. (*No wonder—it's a bummer.*) We have intercourse only once every two weeks on the average. I think that low level of activity is probably due to my anxiety about the general situation. I have failed to reach orgasm so many times I almost hate to try again. It seems easier not to try at all than to be disappointed, than to take the time and emoional energy to try and fail again.

"This problem has been present since the beginning of our relationship. I began to seriously worry about it after we'd been married for a year. Up to the present time in our attempts to improve the situation, we've both done a fair amount of reading and a lot of talking. In addition, I've sought professional help from a total of eight different doctors, seven of whom are psychiatrists. As a result, I learned a lot about myself and a lot about psychiatrists. The insight I've gained about myself and my partner and our interrelationship has improved the overall quality of our marriage, but hasn't really been of much significant help to our sexual togetherness. Our sexual relationship has improved slowly over the years, but I think this may be just as due to twelve years of maturity on our parts as to any of the psychiatric help I've received. One of the men I consulted suggested that I just fake orgasms. To me this seems totally unacceptable and, indeed, a terrible insult to a serious man-woman relationship. (*Asset: She's totally purposefull.*)

"I should probably be more specific about the nature of the improvement I spoke of. In the very early years of our marriage, I found sex physically and emotionally not only distasteful, but also very, very unpleasant and almost abhorrent. I hated it. Physically it was uncomfortable. I'm sure now that was because I had no or little secretion, so all I got was a lot of friction and irritation and soreness. Emotionally I hated it, too. At the present time I find sex usually not unpleasant, either emotionally or physically. Sometimes it's pleasant. Very rarely it's wonderful. (*Asset: She's experienced her goal and may re-create it.*)

"I'm coming for counseling now in hopes that you can help me find how to have good sex with my husband before we both go nuts. (*Easy. First it requires defining and describing.*)

"Ever since he read Masters and Johnson's first report, he has wanted to seek their type of counseling. He felt it would probably be very effective. (*Asset: She has a supportive, purposefull partner.*) I've been the one who resisted. I suppose for several reasons. One of them, of course, being that the psychiatrists were all rather opposed to that type of therapy. (*Seems to me that since they were of little help, their advice might have been questioned.*) Also, I felt that the idea of telling one more person the history of the problem and all that was perhaps more than I care to go through again. When an article appeared in *Newsweek*, the cover story about the new type of sexual counseling, they mentioned that most of the people who went to Masters and Johnson already had been in some sort of psychotherapy. (*Hopefullness: She's experienced renewed expectation.*) I was very interested and very surprised at this. My husband said it made sense because the type of people who would be motivated to seek psychiatric help would also be the type who would probably be motivated to go see someone like Masters and Johnson.

"The major source of sexual information for me was my mother, whose attitude can best be summarized as anti-man. She and my father had and have a lousy marriage. My mother feels men are out to get and to use women. She views being a wife and mother as the worst of all possible roles. (*Possible liability: What a crummy model Theresa had.*)

"My adult sexual experience began with my husband. We met when I was a freshman at college and he was a junior. We became engaged in the fall of my sophomore year and began having sexual relations about the same time. At that time, couples were automatically thrown out of school if they were caught in sexual relationships, and I worried a great deal about the possibility of being discovered. But I also felt very warm and secure in the good love I knew we had. (*Asset, asset, asset.*) I might add that my mother decided that we were having sexual relations long before we actually did and told several of our neighbors so. I remember thinking: Well, if she's telling everyone we are, why not?

"After six years of marriage, our sexual relationship was

still lousy, and I had become convinced there was something the matter with me. We decided that having an affair would be one way for me to find out. In retrospect, that seems a pretty immature approach to our problem (*and rather common, nonetheless*), but we were pretty immature at that time, at least in this area.

"You asked me to fantasize about an ideal sexual relationship, and that makes me feel uncomfortable. I suppose that's because I would fantasize about a relationship with someone, anyone, other than my husband. And I suppose that's because I'd really like to start fresh without that albatross of twelve years of major and minor sexual disasters hovering over the bed. I know how I'd feel at the end—like a giant smile button, extremely satisfied with myself and the world and thinking I'm pretty magnificent. I know because the two or three times in my life when I have had wonderful sex, I've felt that way."

(*Theresa feels that way often these days. She learned how to become response-able. How? The couple got interested in sensual massage at first. Theresa did not enjoy the concept of learning to stimulate herself, so the "Learning about self-stimulation" tape was of little help to her. I asked her if she would mind going to a licensed physical therapist for massage. She shrugged and agreed. Of course the therapist left sex alone and had the woman get in touch with her body in a nonsexual way. In this way she learned about pleasure through the art of touch. Her husband went with her on the second visit and watched, learning through modeling how to do for Theresa what the therapist did. At first she kept her panties on, and her husband—still following the therapist's model—refrained from sexual touch. But soon Theresa removed her panties and her husband's touch became gently sexual. In opening herself up in a trusting way to intimacy and the new adaptive skills that they learned, and allowing her husband to touch her, Theresa experienced orgasm. In time, he substituted his penis for his hand, and soon after that she was enjoying orgasm through intercourse. People who think self-stimulation is wrong may stimulate themselves using other people's body parts rather than their own. They needn't ever masturbate.*)

BARBARA

Barbara was the 27-year-old wife of a movie theater owner and the mother of three children of preschool age.

"My problem is simply that I cannot reach a climax. It's not as simple as that, really—it's much more involved. It started out simply, though. When I got married I had not had intercourse with anyone except my husband. I'd had lots of sexual experiences, but everything was short of penis-in-vagina. I enjoyed the excitement of sex very much with my husband. (*Asset: She likes sex and is really widely experienced already.*)

"The first time we had intercourse, about a year before we were married, it was kind of a disappointment for me. I expected to feel all sorts of things, including guilt, because all my life I had thought this is going to be so neat. It was okay, but not that superspecial. (*Could have turned right around and made it better than okay the next time.*)

"I continued to have intercourse without climax, and I didn't tell my husband until after we were married a year. He was surprised. I'm a pretty good actress. (*Liability: She was faking instead of participating.*) Now I think I should have kept my mouth shut and gone on being an actress. Ever since I told my husband, it's only gotten complicated, because now he feels frustration, and I don't feel much like doing it.

"I don't know how to describe it. I can talk about sex. I can feel sexy feelings toward people, all this sort of thing, but it only becomes a problem when it comes right down to the actual moment. And then I do most everything to avoid the situation. (*Asset: Like so many others, she has great power and uses it to shut down or turn off, rather than rev up and turn on.*) I don't know how this got started. I never said no to my husband, but I do everything I can think of practically to avoid it. (*Because she expects to fail again.*) We still have sex fairly often, three, sometimes four times a week. Whenever I feel the inevitable coming, and that's the way I feel about it, I know I feel terrible thoughts about my husband. I just want to scream at him. I just want to crawl inside my skin. I say things that I think will put him off. I enjoy taking care of him. I enjoy being a wife and mother, and I think I am a good wife except in the area of sex.

"What do I want? I'd like to be able to just look at my husband and think, 'Ummmm, I'd like to jump into bed with you right now.' (*Asset: The tone of her voice indicated she was half turned on just thinking about this.*) Or like when he whispers little things in my ear like, 'Let's go to bed and screw,' I'd like to get all excited and say, 'Ummm, let's go!' Instead, I feel annoyed or disgusted. (*It's time to learn new responses.*)

"What have I done? I read every book I could get my hands on—*The Sensuous Man, The Sensuous Woman*, you name it. Sometimes I got excited reading, but I learned nothing new. (*Could have him read these and other books to her.*) I went to a doctor and he told me to just be good to my husband, don't expect a climax. Sometime after that I casually mentioned it to another doctor and he recommended a book. I said I'd read it. Then he suggested maybe I should see a psychiatrist. I don't think I need that. I'm not screwed up. Finally, I found an understanding doctor and he sent me to you. (*Readiness: Despite the most discouraging reaction from doctors one and two, she didn't give up.*)

"When I was in high school I had a lot of boy friends. I was a sort of prom queen type, although twenty or twenty-five pounds overweight. I was everybody's best friend. Everybody described me as 'sweet.' Most of my dates were with boys who weren't going with someone else at the time. They were doing their nice, kind deed. I'm not knocking myself. (*Yes, she is.*) I'm just saying I wasn't a sex object to them. (*I'll bet that's what she wanted to be.*)

"When I went to college, I was going with the quarterback when I was a freshman, but three or four weeks into the relationship he said I had to go all the way or get lost. It shattered me.

"My standards and sights have always been perhaps unrealistically high. The fellows I was interested in weren't interested in me. I had plenty of fellows clamoring on my doorstep, but I guess I was a little snobby. I had high standards for the people I wanted to date. So I didn't get as much experience as my friends.

"I had an experience with a man twelve years older. He was very sensitive and we talked about life and philosophy, but he was too emotionally dependent on me. I was the strong person in the relationship; I felt life would be too complicated with him. My sexual experiences with him were romantic. I didn't screw him, but we had plenty of other experiences. (*Asset: She's on her way.*) I was going with him when I met my husband on a blind date.

"Another thing . . . about my husband. We're on different time schedules. I need sleep and just have to go to bed. When there were late parties in school I'd be asleep on the couch in the middle of the party. Now we go to people's houses for dinner and I have to splash water on my face and do jumping jacks to stay awake. I'm a zombie at night. My whole family is like that—my mother, my sister, everybody. But my husband comes alive in the late afternoon and is a night person. (*One of them could learn to change by modeling the other.*)

"I guess all our schedules are different. He's involved in

civic things and he takes a class at night and sometimes works late. I'm involved with social activities and I hold offices in clubs and organizations. There are plenty of evenings when we're not in the house together. (*Liability: They are not making it easy.*)

"My ideal fantasy? I don't know why, but it's very hard for me to fantasize. Oh, I shouldn't say that. I do it all day long. But sexual fantasy . . . I just can't do it today. Maybe I can do it later. I just can't think of anything that I want to fantasize about. I feel turned off about sex. I guess if I was going to have a fantasy it would be that I could get raced up in bed over sex." (*Asset: Her voice dropped, became more sensual, showing readiness.*)

(I shared with Barbara a learning theory I've developed —but haven't tried to prove—about why every survey ever conducted shows that more men than women masturbate. The reason is . . . right from the very beginning, males are permitted to touch their genitals more often than females. There are times, in fact, when the little boy is even encouraged to touch himself—when he is learning how to stand up and use a toilet and is directed in how to aim and afterward how to shake off the last droplets of urine before putting his penis back in his pants. However, the little girl is never allowed to touch herself, except when washing, and even then Mom sternly urges the child to hurry about it. When small girls begin to play with themselves, moms nervously look for rashes and sores, and the little girl is told to stop. Little boys are also told to stop . . . but they are still allowed to touch themselves when they pee.

Barbara listened to this theory and followed some of the specific suggestions noted parenthetically above—for example, having her partner read some of those sensual books to her. She also viewed a videotape of someone like her, learning how to experience an orgasm. She got in touch with her feelings in ways she had not experienced before. She learned that she, like nearly everyone else—male as well as female—was stuck in cognition, thinking everything rather than really feeling it. Once she saw where she was stuck, she moved over. She learned to experience orgasm, at first alone and then with someone else.)

CHAPTER
19
"I Can't Come Vaginally"

And the woman might ask, "Is it important that I do?" The answer to that one is no—only if you make it important.

The next question is, "Could I, if I wanted to?" And the answer to that one is, yes, if you wish.

MELINDA

Melinda was 37 and recently divorced, following 13 years of marriage. She had three children, rented a room in her house and worked as a part-time librarian to supplement the child support and alimony that arrived so irregularly.

"I am pushing forty and am having trouble having an orgasm with a partner. I have had this trouble all my life. Actually, I have had an orgasm, but only a couple of times.

In almost forty years that's not much. (*Another winner
dressed as a loser.*)

"The first time was when I was about nineteen years
old and I went to the beach with a boy and we engaged
in necking and petting, and it was just through physical
contact, he was lying on top of me, and from just the
physical contact, I had an orgasm. (*That's how fast it was!*)
I can remember it distinctly. And then a year later, after
I graduated, again I went out with a boy. I had gone out
with him many times, I liked him. I remember we had
gone to the beach again, and coming home he put his head
on my lap and began what you might call oral sex on his
part and again I had an orgasm. (*Asset: The beach seems
to be a positive setting. Revisiting or recreating a successful setting from the past may work again and again.
Melinda could take her present partner to the beach if
she wished.*)

"About six months later I started dating a boy whom I
later married, and we went in for kissing and necking and
petting, but we did not have intercourse. I insisted upon
being a virgin when we married. So we were married and
intercourse took place, and I did not have an orgasm that
way. In about six months, it became obvious to him. And
that's the way it basically went for thirteen years. (*And of
course she would not tell him how she did experience
orgasm in the past at the beach with the other two partners.*) During the past five years he put me down as being
sexually inadequate. By then I really wasn't interested in
having sex. I had sex only to please my husband.

"Since my breakup with my husband, I have had relations with three other men. The first was shortly after the
separation. I think it was just plain curiosity: Could I
have an orgasm with someone who wasn't my husband?
(*Yes, if she set it up right.*) I picked as a partner someone
I knew casually, a gentleman who was a few years older,
and I came to find out that he had more hang-ups about

having a penis that is mainly too small than I had about having an orgasm. He was good for my ego, but not much else.

"The next encounter was about six months later when I met another person who was enjoyable, who seemed to enjoy my mind and my character. He didn't have any hang-ups, but still I did not have an orgasm, although we tried twice. (*Did they go to the beach? Did he lie on top of her? Did he have what she might call "oral sex"?*)

"Both of these men were married, by the way, and I knew at the time it was leading no place, but I was having curiosity that I wish I'd had at nineteen years of age, along with birth control pills. (*Asset: She may respond differently when a relationship is leading someplace. Here she knows what doesn't work.*)

"The last time, there was another six months' lapse and I met a gentleman who is not married, but I know it will go no place, too. I'm having the relationship only for the self-satisfaction it brings me in building my ego; that someone thinks of me as a woman, who can sexually arouse me. But so far, no orgasm.

"I very much want to have a feeling that I am normal in all respects and I want to feel that I can enjoy sex. I realize now something I wish I had realized twenty years ago— although there is a heck of a lot more to life than sex, sex is very important in life; it can bring much enjoyment and much fulfillment and it can bring a closeness to people. To have a fulfilled man-woman relationship, which I hope someday to have, you must have several planes of communication. (*Readiness and purposefullness: She knows what she wants. She is full of intention.*)

"Both of my parents had poor relationships with their own parents and they had poor relationships between themselves. My mother was constantly ill. She had a hysterectomy when I was very young and then a nervous breakdown which put her in a private sanitarium for a while.

She had several tumors and finally had a mastectomy. Several years later, when I was in my late teens, she had an aneurysm and survived that, only to later die of a kidney failure.

"My father was an alcoholic who died of cirrhosis of the liver. He did not share the same bed with my mother. After she had her mastectomy, she always had her own room. My father was gone a lot. I was glad. He was a salesman and he always had a lot of business meetings at night. After my mother passed away, I found out the meetings were girl friends."

However gloomy a picture Melinda painted of her past and present, when she stepped into the future—into fantasy—the prospects brightened.

"Right now I do have orgasms by myself using a vibrator, and when I'm doing that I fantasize. I picture myself maybe in a glamorous negligee, in a very romantic mood with a past male acquaintance, maybe one of the boys I went out with before I was married, or the last two men I've had sexual relations with since my divorce—never with my husband. (*That's good. You're not married to him anymore.*) At that time we were having foreplay, petting, touching, leading up to having intercourse. (*Asset: She is so close . . .*) At this point in my fantasy, I have an orgasm with the vibrator. Always with a vibrator I do have an orgasm."

(*Melinda typifies what went into* The Hite Report. *I learned from patients what Shere Hite learned from her survey people—that many women learn to experience orgasm by "touch," and that's very different from men, who learn to experience orgasm by "containment." She responds to [and is rewarded by] touch, and he responds to [and is rewarded by] containment. It is a perfect example of Pavlovian conditioning. And the expectation for them* to come together in perfect union, or even for the woman to come at all during intercourse, may be unreasonable. He enters her and experiences containment. He has learned to experience orgasm that way and she has not—because nothing may be touching her where she likes to be touched. Now she is in the classic double bind experienced by so many nonorgasmic women. She thinks something is wrong with her, and he begins to think he's not doing it right; both believe they are inadequate.

This is a major source of problems among men and women. The truth of it all is that if she's learned one way— by touch—and he's learned another—by containment— they could communicate that to one another and combine the two and both have a big win. She could use her hands during intercourse; he could use his hands. Melinda began to use creative fantasies with her vibrator, replacing it in her mind with her partner's penis as she approached orgasm, finally replacing it in fact—while stimulating her clitoris simultaneously, or having it stimulated by her partner. Thus she, too, learned to get in touch with her body, her feelings.)

20

Turning on the Machine

In the treatment of sexual problems it has been found that you, the client, are the true expert in knowing about you and about your problems. It has also been found that the therapist—or counselor, or facilitator, or friend, or whatever—can best help you to explore new solutions if he (or she) is well informed about how you see the problem, and how you think it became of concern to you.

Similarly, you can best help *yourself* if the same conditions prevail. If recognizing that a problem exists is the first step toward resolution, and being in a state of readiness is step number two, then it follows that description and communication are steps number three and four. This chapter will assist you in describing the problem and then communicating it to someone else, if you choose to go that route, now or at some later date, or perhaps just to yourself.

When I tell my clients I'm going to teach them how to talk to themselves, they often look at me as if I was slightly off-balance. Several have even said words to the effect that, "Are you kidding me? This problem's already got me talking to myself! I don't need you for *that*."

Perhaps not. By the time we have reached, oh, say, 21 years of age—and many a lot sooner of course—most of us have talked to ourselves often and long enough to have gotten good at it. Or at least we think we have. We can all get better.

Here's something else: How many of us know how to *listen* to what we say?

The first time Laura heard herself was when she was interviewed by one of her local television newsmen. It was one of those man-in-the-street surveys that television is always doing, and when Laura turned on her set that night, she said she noticed the way she looked and the *way* she spoke, but she didn't notice *what* she said.

"Oh," she cried, "my dress looks awful, and my hair!" She paused. "My voice is terrible, so nasal . . ."

This chapter is aimed at helping you listen to the truly terrific things you could say.

Of course this will be accomplished in the same way my clients do it—by making a cassette tape.

WHY MAKE A CASSETTE?

There are many reasons for making a cassette.

1. Merely thinking about things doesn't seem to be enough. If you're just thinking, your thoughts go pfffft, and you can't get a handle on them. Thoughts may disappear as quickly as they are thought. And memory is a tricky thing; no one can recall everything he or she ever thought. Writing it down is one way of hanging on to the thought. But this is 1978, and you might do it better than

"Dear Diary . . ." I mean, "Dear Diary" *takes time*, especially if you think somebody's going to read it someday, and you want to punctuate it correctly and you want to dot all the i's and cross all the t's and make it look pretty. Well, you don't have to do all that when you use a tape recorder.

2. Many have never spoken their problems or complaints aloud, not even to a close friend. Actually, verbalizing the problem may itself constitute an act of resolution, moving the troubled reader toward the zero-to-plus-ten side of life's scale.

3. Similarly, most of us have never really listened to ourselves, and when we thought we *were* listening—as when Laura watched and listened to herself on TV—the words weren't getting through. After you make the tape, you should listen to it, again and again and again. If you hear something you want to change, resist the temptation, please. Let it stand, and add a postscript at the end. Then add another postscript if you wish. But please do not erase any of the original tape. If you change your mind about something you said earlier, hearing what you originally said and then hearing what you thought (or felt) a few minutes later will be helpful all by itself. For now you are into the "process" of change. Listening to the tape repeatedly will allow you to truly hear yourself, perhaps for the first time.

4. Later on you may wish to made additional, follow-up tapes; many clients do. Comparing the tapes may be helpful. Listening first to the original tape and then to the follow-up tape may help to give you some measure of self-growth and understanding.

5. If you seek outside assistance from a therapist or counselor, now or later, the tapes may make the issues at hand clearer to this person. Listening again to the tape at some future time may help this person recall detailed information that in a conversation might be lost to mem-

ory. And time spent at home thinking about the problems while preparing the tape can save treatment hours and thereby lessen expenses for you.

MAKING THE TAPE

The concerned/interested/involved reader has taken the first steps toward resolution of his or her problem(s) merely by reading this book—by being exposed to sexual winners as they presented themselves on cassettes of their own. Now it's the reader's turn to learn for himself, and *from* himself.

You need some "hardware"—a recorder and a tape. If you do not presently own a cassette recorder and do not wish to buy one (they're available for as little as $30 to $40), perhaps you have a friend who has one. Or you know someone who might have access to one at work. Some people have them in their cars. Others have them in combination with their hi-fi sets and portable radios. Cassette recorders may also be rented and are available from some libraries and YMCA's. Many civic organizations and churches also will make them accessible to their members and parishioners. The point is, cassette recorders are nearly everywhere.

You also need a 45- or 60-minute cassette tape, available from your neighborhood drug, hi-fi, record, or discount store for as little as 80 or 90 cents, seldom more than three or four dollars. (The more expensive ones are designed to record music, not talk.) You probably will use only thirty minutes of tape. However, if you feel you need more time, please turn the tape over and continue on side two. Many people talk for a full hour.

Read over the instructions before recording. Notice that the questions listed below only suggest areas you might wish to think about while describing your problem. You need not feel restricted or limited by them. Think of them as guidelines, please. The important thing is to say it the way you feel it and think it and do it. The questions below are only suggestions to help you think about what concerns you and how you feel about those concerns. If you find the questions are not helpful to you, *ignore them.* Remember, when it comes to talking about you, you are the expert.

Use your own words and state the problem in a way that is comfortable for you. Pauses and hesitations are okay, so please do not worry about them. If you get stuck for a moment and don't know what to say next, stop the machine. Then when you have collected your thoughts, "TURN ON" again.

Couples, please note: Make your tapes separately and do not discuss these first tapes with each other. You may wish to take your tape to a counselor or therapist, and he or she may want each of you to have an equal opportunity to discuss the problem freely from *your* viewpoint. This can also be a good opportunity for you to state your feelings openly and honestly without fear of hurting (or being hurt by) your partner, for the tape need never be heard by your partner. Should you think this unfair, make a second tape intended for your partner. You might notice a difference in content.

If you wish to exchange tapes with your partner on another occasion, fine. Where at first you might not be able to talk so openly face to face, the first tape may serve as an excellent tool to open those closed channels. But— make the first tape for yourself. Complete honesty is essential.

After making the tape, listen to it again and again to see if there are any additions you wish to make. You might even wish to take notes while listening. Just add further comments at the end of your tape and then listen again. Please do not erase or rerecord any portions. For those among you who would like to play "psychoanalyst"—you can sit behind your couch and put the machine on it. Turn it off whenever you feel insightful.

THE TAPE GUIDELINES

It may be helpful to read the following questions, or guidelines, all the way through before beginning to record.

1. *Describe, as best you can, your problem. Be as specific and descriptive as possible, about it.*

    How do you think it came about?

    When and how often does it occur? Describe situations when it seems to be of most concern.

    How long has it been present? When did you first notice it?

    What would you do without it?

2. *How have you handled the problem so far?*

    What have you done about the problem by yourself?

    Have you talked with your partner, gone to friends, experimented sexually, read books?

    Have you sought other professional help? If so, where?

    What have been the results of this effort?

3. *What do you want for yourself? Be specific in stating your goal (one at a time, please).*

4. *How did you learn about "sex"?*

    Who taught you?

What attitudes or actions did they encourage or discourage?

(Sources of information usually include parents, religion, other family members, friends, schools, books. Discuss the sources you feel were, and now are, the most influential in the development of your current problem.)

5. *Think about your past experiences, those related specifically to your unique problem.*

Examples might be: child sex games, self-stimulation, opposite-sex encounters, same-sex encounters.

How do you feel about them now?

Recall and describe all the different types of experiences you've had.

Did anyone else know about your activities? If yes, what was their response?

Under what circumstances did these activities take place: i.e., in secret, openly, with others, alone, on dates, within marriage, outside marriage?

Do you feel any of these prior experiences are connected with your current problem? In what way?

How often do you have sexual fantasies? Do you enjoy them? Do they disturb you? Describe them.

Are you aware of having sexual dreams? Describe them. Do you experience orgasm in your dreams?

6. *Are there other factors which you think may be adding to your problem? For example: work, separation, children, beliefs, attitudes, feelings, considerations, etc.*

7. *Fantasize for a moment what the ideal sexual relationship would be for you. (Or how you might be without your problem.) Be as detailed as possible.*

> Where are you?
> What time is it?
> Who are you with?
> What is happening?
> How does it end?
> How might it begin again?

HOW TO REVIEW YOUR TAPE

Once you have finished talking into the machine—perhaps by now you'll regard the recorder as a friend—you'll want to listen all the way through. As you do so, you might wish to notice a number of things.

1. Notice *"where you're at."*

Where are you on the scale of Leftsidedness and Rightsidedness? And where are you stuck? Are you stuck cognitively—in desire, in motivation, in thinking? (As noted earlier, most of those who are stuck are stuck here; we think too much. It's called mind-fucking.) Or, are you stuck affectively—in arousal, in participation, in feeling? Are you stuck motorically—in orgasm, in intense excitement, in doing? Are you stuck in more than one place? Remember that we need to notice where we are before we can go somewhere else. And remember that we need to know *why* we are stuck. (That's getting stuck in "figuring it out.")

2. Notice *your liabilities.*

These are the "bad habits," the "didn'ts," the stuff that gets in the way, what a friend of mine once called "the hair in the drain," that which causes the flow to stop, that which causes things to get stuck. Of course, hair in the drain must be removed before the flow of water is resumed. The nice thing about human behavior is we needn't even worry about the "hair in the drain"—all we need to do is notice that it's there and then leave it alone and get on with living. We needn't try to "unlearn"—or wipe out—something. All we need to do is learn something new, add new behavior to our repertoire. Skills and bad habits can coexist, and either can be chosen. A person who desires to modify behavior need only acquire a new behavior and then select it for use when appropriate.

3. Notice your assets.

This is the good stuff. These are the skills (often unnoticed until now), the things that work or have worked in the past. The "dids." If liabilities were what kept us in Leftsidedness, or zero-to-minus-ten sex, then assets are those items of behavior which are on the other side of life, zero-to-*plus*-10 Rightsidedness. (It is possible to be on both sides at the same time.) Assets also are the means by which we may leave Leftsidedness alone forever. Assets are the thinking, feeling, and doing behavior that can be used again and again (even if they haven't been used recently) and can be built upon or expanded.

4. Notice your readiness.

Readiness is the will to believe, the belief in the Enchanted Cottage, the awareness of Rightsidedness, even when stuck in Leftsidedness; it is a glimpse into the future. Aristotle said, "All that we do is done with an eye to something else." Readiness recognizes that there *is* something else. It is not the games people play, but the games people *could* play. It is not *déjà vu*, but *future* view.

5. *Notice your purposefullness.*

Purposefullness is being full of purpose. Purpose is
(quoting my friend, the Oxford Dictionary) "that which
one sets before oneself as a thing to be done or attained."
It is goal. It is intention, resolution, determination. It is
meaning to do something. It is the result or effect intended
or sought. It is the end, the aim. That's purpose. Purposefullness is being full of that. It is being clear about what
you want. Notice if your purpose (intention) is good.
(Good means responsible, that's all.) America's preemi-
nent essayist, Ralph Waldo Emerson said, "A good intention clothes itself with sudden power. When a god wishes
to ride, any chip or pebble will bud and shoot out winged
feet and serve him for a horse." You may be served as well.

6. *Notice your hopefullness.*

Hopefullness is being full of hope. Hope is desire plus
expectation. In a way, it is the blend of purposefullness and
readiness—knowing what you want and believing there is
a chance you can get it. Hopefullness is being powered by
Norman Vincent Peale's positive thinking and adding aux-
iliary jets—*positive feeling* and *positive doing*. It is the
belief in the possibility of an antigravity machine, a process
which swears that everything that goes up doesn't have to
come down. It is losers believing they could be winners
so hard that they think they *will* be winners. They think
they *are winners.* Usually it is a place reached after going
through a period of indecisiveness: yes, no, yes, no, maybe,
yes, yes, yes! Did you know we *are* all winners, anyway?

7. *Notice your fantasies.*

Readiness recognizes the existence of the future. Purposefullness focuses your sights on the future, makes a

part of the future your own personal goal. Hopefullness leads you to believe it's going to happen. Fantasy encompasses all three. Creating a productive fantasy is putting your future to work for you. "Lord knows, why not?" a client said. "My past sure has been exerting its influence; why not give my future equal time?"

CHAPTER

21

Turning Yourself On

Most sex therapists these days suggest a number of exercises or positions or psychological prescriptions—potions and notions and incredible tricks that work for some, but not all. One of my colleagues, Jack Annon, a psychologist with a successful practice, has written what is probably the most comprehensive survey of all these practical and proved approaches to sex therapy.*

I think all the stuff in Jack's book is terrific. Paradoxical intention and successive approximation (two of many psychological approaches) . . . the "stuffing technique" developed by Masters and Johnson for impotence problems and the Kegel exercises for a woman's orgasm problems (to name two physical methods) . . . the vibrators and pneumatic erector sets (mechanical techniques) . . .

* Jack S. Annon, *The Behavioral Treatment of Sexual Problems*, New York, Harper & Row, 1976.

I love it all. And I use a lot of these ideas when they seem appropriate, as is evidenced in the composite audio cassettes I have my clients listen to. Yet I believe there is something stronger than all the psychological and physical and mechanical devices in the world . . . and that is a way of looking at life, a special point of view. (One which is supported by the tapes, I believe, as well as presented throughout this book.)

—I believe that noticing where you are in the Rating Game, noticing where you are on the minus-ten to plus-ten scale, can put you in a position to change your position, prepare you for your journey from Leftsidedness to Rightsidedness, blaze trails for future exploration of your neglected intuitive, artistic brain.

—I believe that noticing where you are stuck in the DAO (Desire/Arousal/Orgasm) cycle of life—noticing whether you're stuck in thinking, feeling, or doing; noticing if it is a lack of motivation, stunted participation, or nonexistent excitement that is making you a loser—can make it possible for you to get unstuck.

—I believe that noticing your liabilities—your "didn'ts" —and recognizing them for what they are, things that *do not work* in your life, will permit you to leave them alone and move on to something else.

—I believe that noticing your assets—the "dids"—and recognizing *them* for what they are, things that *did work* once in your life, will make it abundantly clear that they may be used again and again, in their original or brand-new forms.

—I believe that noticing your potential—your "coulds" —and recognizing the vast array of options and possibilities that lie before you (perhaps until now unseen) may provide the specific answers to any and all of your problems.

—I believe that noticing your readiness, your willingness and openness to change, can make change possible.

—I believe that noticing your purposefullness and your clear sense of intention to accomplish a specific goal will make that goal attainable.

—I believe that noticing your hopefullness, being full of desire (easy) and expectation (not as easy), can set it up, can make it a piece of cake.

—I believe that noticing your imagination, your ability to create a productive fantasy, can make your wildest, most joyous dreams come true.

I believe these things, in concert, can work not just for the few, or even for the many, but for *everyone*. I further believe that everyone already has most of these characteristics. Many merely seem to be in a dormant, or undeveloped, state.

It may take time to notice and develop some of the others. Remember that people learn at different speeds. Some may require considerable practice. But it all works and it's all fun because you only practice the good stuff, the stuff that thinks good, the stuff that feels good, the stuff that does good.

You see, the simple truth is, sex feels very good. Why else do we keep doing it? To continue the human race? I suppose some do it for that, and I guess some more do it because they want to continue their own family lines, and still others do it because they think it's expected of them, and so on. But most people do it because it does feel very good. And for those for whom it doesn't feel good (yet), it *could*.

I think that what I want people to get is to understand what losers are, and that anyone who has learned to lose has that as an asset. Anyone who can learn to lose can learn to win. Most of us see ourselves as losers. As kids we learned that. As kids we all heard that we could always do things better. Very early we learned that we didn't

know when and where to go to the bathroom and we
didn't know how to feed ourselves, or stand up and walk
and talk. (Later we learned that we talked too much.)
Throughout life we have been told over and over again
by our parents and other relatives and teachers and
preachers and a thousand more that we weren't doing it
right. We were losers. That's the uncomfortable conclusion we reached.

The truth is, we're all winners at heart. After all, winning and losing are just points of view. And everywhere
you look the points of view conflict and contradict.

About winning, for example . . . the ancient Roman
philosopher Seneca said winning (success) was "insig-
nificant," and never satisfying . . . the poet Robert Louis
Stevenson called it "disenchanting" . . . and Bertrand
Russell believed it made the winner "a prey to boredom,"
while essayist Arthur Kronenberger wrote that the technique of winning was shoddy, the terms ignoble, the
tenure startlingly brief.

Of course, there's disagreement. Somerset Maugham
said winning improved man's character and the Greek
tragedian Euripides concluded that winning gave the
winner a reputation for judgment. "A minute's success,"
the poet Robert Browning wrote, "pays the failure of years."

About losing and losers there is no more agreement.
Another poet, W. H. Auden, wrote that "in life, the loser's
score is always zero," and Arthur Kronenberger, who spoke
so ignobly of success, vented his spleen about failure when
he wrote, "We are neurotically haunted by the imminence,
and by the ignominy, of failure. We know at how frightening a cost one succeeds: to fail is something too awful to
think about."

Others don't attach so much importance to losing. The
actress Rosalind Russell said, "Flops are a part of life's
menu and I've never been a girl to miss out on any of the
courses." And essayist Elbert Hubbard said, "The line be-

tween failure and success is so fine that we scarcely know when we pass it; so fine that we are often on the line and do not know it."

The points of view go on and on and on. And every one of them is valid. Remember—they are only points of view. Given the choice of selecting whichever one is wished, isn't it odd that so many have become losers? And *stayed* losers?

Winning can be so easy! If you think of yourself as a loser and want to change, all you have to notice is that what makes change possible is only its recognition.

It's true. Change is all around us. That's all there really is. Absolutely *nothing* is static. Our bodies are like the flowers, the trees, and the water. They're dynamic. They're mobile. They're vibrant. If you watch sperm under a microscope, you'll notice that they're not sitting around waiting for the bell. If you look at dust under that same microscope, you'll notice what is called the Brownian particle movement. There is constant change, in everything on and off the earth.

That's the way it is. I mean, join in. You might as well. You're already there.

All the losers described in the book are better now. Those who didn't experience orgasms, do. Those who didn't experience erections, do. The few I've met who didn't experience erections at all and couldn't and can't, have learned to experience pleasure again by serving themselves and others in other ways, and they do that now. Those who came too fast learned to come slower. Those who learned to hate their wives, their husbands, themselves, others, have learned to be the way they wish to be. The vast majority—not all—are now like they wanted to be; or if not, they've learned that they did not wish to be that way.

Remember, you are a winner. Or can be if you wish to be. Get into a contemplative state and repeat after me:

"I am truly remarkable, I am truly wonderful . . ." Now say it again and again—and if you have orgasms, say it while experiencing them. After all, there is no rule that says you can't learn to use your orgasms well. Up your orgasm!

Final page, final paragraph, final quotation—from John F. Kennedy: "Change is the law of life. And those who look only to the past or the present are certain to miss the future."